WIRED FOR SUCCESS

12 STEPS TO CREATING A BRAIN HEALTHY LIFE AND ENHANCING EVERYTHING YOU DO

DANIEL G. AMEN, M.D.

MindWorks Press
A Division of Amen Clinics, Inc.

Other Books By Dr. Daniel Amen

Change Your Brain, Change Your Body, Harmony Books, 2010

Magnificent Mind at Any Age, Harmony Books, 2009

Sex on the Brain, Harmony Books, 2007

Making a Good Brain Great, Harmony Books, 2005, Amazon Book of the Year

Preventing Alzheimer's, with neurologist William R. Shankle, M.D., Putnam, 2004

Healing Anxiety and Depression, with Lisa Routh, M.D., Putnam, 2003

New Skills for Frazzled Parents, MindWorks Press, 2003

Healing the Hardware of the Soul, Free Press, 2002

Images of Human Behavior: A Brain SPECT Atlas, MindWorks Press, 2003

Healing ADD, Putnam, 2001

How to Get out of Your Own Way, MindWorks Press, 2000

Change Your Brain, Change Your Life, Three Rivers Press, 1999, New York Times Bestseller

ADD in Intimate Relationships, MindWorks Press, 1997

Would You Give 2 Minutes a Day to a Lifetime of Love?, St. Martin's Press, 1996

A Child's Guide to ADD, MindWorks Press, 1996

A Teenagers Guide to ADD, with Antony Amen and Sharon Johnson, MindWorks Press, 1995

Mindcoach: Teaching Kids To Think Positive And Feel Good, MindWorks Press, 1994

The Most Important Thing in Life I Learned from a Penguin, MindWorks Press, 1994

Ten Steps to Building Values Within Children, MindWorks Press, 1994

The Secrets of Successful Students, MindWorks Press, 1994

Healing the Chaos Within, MindWorks Press, 1993

MEDICAL DISCLAIMER
The information presented in this book is the result of years of practical experience and clinical research by the author. The information in this book, by necessity, is of a general nature and not a substitute for an evaluation or treatment by a competent medical specialist. If you believe you are in need of medical interventions please see a medical practitioner as soon as possible. The stories in this book are true. The names and circumstances of the stories have been changed to protect the anonymity of patients.

Dedication

To Elias, my newly born grandson.
There is no better time to start this journey than now.

Table of Contents

INTRODUCTION

How Your Brain Either Helps or Hurts Success In All You Do

Your brain is involved in everything you do. When your brain works right, you work right, and when your brain is troubled, you have trouble in your life. It is your brain that brings love, success, and health into your life; and it is brain dysfunction, in large part, that ruins your body and limits your success.

Consider the following:

- It is your brain that decides to get you out of bed in the morning to exercise, to give you a stronger, leaner body, or it is your brain that causes you to hit the snooze button to procrastinate your workout.

- It is your brain that pushes you away from the table telling you that you have had enough, or it is your brain that gives you permission to have the second bowl of Rocky Road ice cream, making you look and feel like a blob.

- It is your brain that keeps you focused on your work so you complete assignments on time and get promoted, or it is your brain that lets you become easily distracted so you fail to do a good job and get passed up for promotions.

- It is your brain that helps you be a loving and supportive spouse and parent, or it is your brain that may be at the root of conflict in your relationships.

- It is your brain that manages the stress in your life and relaxes you so that you look vibrant, or it is your brain that when left unchecked, sends stress signals to the rest of your body that wrinkles your skin and makes your belly fat.

- It is your brain that turns away cigarettes, too much caffeine or alcohol, or it is your brain that gives you permission to smoke, to have that third cup of coffee, or that third glass of wine, thus making every system in your body look and feel old.

- And it is your brain that allows you to make and keep friends at school, or it is your brain that makes it hard for you to get along with schoolmates.

Your brain is the command and control center of your life and your body. If you want a better life and a better body, the first place to ALWAYS start is by having a better brain.

Based on my brain-imaging work with tens of thousands of patients from 75 different countries over the past 20 years, I have developed a simple, personalized program to help you change your brain to improve your body and your life.

The program is comprised of five simple steps.

1. Take the simple, personalized evaluation – Dr. Amen's Change Your Brain, Change Your Body Questionnaire (www.amenclinics.com/cybcyb). My research clearly shows that one program does not work for everyone. This will take about 30 minutes to complete.

2. Basic and Individually Tailored Recommendations – There are several basic recommendations that are helpful for all of us, such as a multiple vitamin, fish oil, and balancing blood sugar and cravings. Then based on your results, you are given a personalized set of recommendations to enhance your own individual brain issues to enhance your life.

3. 12 Steps to Creating a Brain Healthy Life – Several, simple skills are essential to creating a brain healthy life. You will find these 12 steps in this short book.

4. Track and record your progress with *Dr. Amen's Change Your Brain, Change Your Body Daily Journal* and gain support of an online community at www.amenclinics.com/cybcyb.

5. Follow up – After 12 weeks, retake Dr. Amen's Change Your Brain, Change Your Body Questionnaire to see what areas still need work. Follow-up is key to helping you create a brain healthy body and program for life.

The Typical American Family

It's 7 a.m. and Lisa is feeling sluggish from half a bottle of wine the night before and five hours of interrupted sleep due to her constant fretting and her husband's snoring. She starts her day with a large cup of coffee, made palatable with artificial sweeteners and preservative-filled fake cream, and two glazed chocolate doughnuts.

She has now tried to wake her two children, Jeff, 14, and Lucy, 10, for the third time. The kids press their parents to stay up late, either playing on their computers or video games. Not wanting to fight with the children, the parents usually just give in to them, but they often struggle to get them up in the morning. Now Lisa is yelling and feeling very irritated. "Why do I have to go through this every morning with these ungrateful kids?" she thinks. It is not uncommon for Lisa to get up 20 minutes later than she wanted.

Most mornings are a race filled with stress. The kids are just so hard, she thinks. She knows the kids will fight her about breakfast and now that they are late again, they will just have to grab doughnuts on the way out the door. Her husband, Jeff, left the house an hour ago to fight the traffic on his way to work. Sleepy, he tries to drink his coffee while talking to a client on his cell phone. So the day starts for many American families — filled with stress, sugar, caffeine, bad fat, artificial sweeteners, and preservatives. These choices hurt their brains and limit their ability to be their best.

12 Steps To Creating A Brain Healthy Life

This short book is about creating a brain healthy life by breaking bad brain habits and replacing them with healthier ones. Creating a brain healthy life is simple and not hard. It is simple because as you will see from the 12 steps in this book, they are not hard to understand or even hard to implement with a little forethought and impulse control. Yet, many societal factors are stacked against us — from the ways businesses advertise to us to peer pressure, to the availability of fast but anti-nutritious food, to great but brain-draining entertainment, to fascinating sleep robbers like the Internet, to the pace of life that makes sickness more likely than health.

This book will give you the information you need to set up a brain healthy program to enhance brain function and subsequently your ability to have a better life, a more successful career, stronger relationships, more money, and improved health. Let's get started on your journey to better brain health!

STEP 1

Love Your Brain

DEVELOP AN EMOTIONAL RELATIONSHIP WITH YOUR BRAIN

The brain is involved in everything you do. At every moment of every day of your life, your brain heavily influences how you think, feel, act, and interact with others. Here are some examples of how the brain influences your behavior.

- When you go to work or school, it is your brain that decides whether you are on time or routinely late.

- When you eat dinner, it is your brain that decides to push you away from the table or allows you to have a third helping of mashed potatoes and gravy.

- When your child is experiencing problems in school or at home, it is your brain that either helps you cope and come up with solutions or react with frustration.

- When your boss dumps a last-minute project on your desk, it is your brain that determines your ability to handle the extra pressure.

- When you interact with family, friends, coworkers, or schoolmates, it is your brain that influences whether you act in a caring, loving way or whether you create discord in your relationships.

The impact of the brain on your life goes even deeper than that. The gray matter between your ears is the essence of your very being — your intelligence, your personality, your character, and even your very soul. The brain influences every part of who you are. It drives your likes and dislikes, hobbies, and talents. Take any and every aspect of your life — work, relationships, religion, physical, and mental health — and you will find your brain at the center of it all.

When your brain works right, you work right. When your brain is troubled, you have trouble in your life. When your brain is healthy, it makes it much easier to be the best you can be — a loving parent, a supportive spouse, a stellar employee, an effective business owner, a great student, a healthy individual. On the other hand, when your brain is troubled, it creates trouble in every aspect of your life. It is harder to get along with each other, to excel in school or at work, to achieve success, or to stick to a healthy diet and exercise program.

Some of the many problems a troubled brain can lead to include:

- A lack of focus
- Procrastination
- Impulsiveness
- Poor memory
- Rigidity
- Anger issues
- Excessive worry
- Lack of motivation
- Poor organizational skills
- Obesity

All of these make it much more difficult to achieve your goals in every area of your life. As a psychiatrist, I have seen thousands of patients struggle in their relationships, at work or school, and in their quest for a healthier and more attractive body due to these problems. When I added brain imaging to my clinical practice in 1991, these brain issues became much more understandable. In our clinics, we use a sophisticated brain-imaging technique, called SPECT, that shows how the brain is functioning so we can better diagnose and treat our patients.

After analyzing scans and then talking with patients, it became clear to me that people with healthy brains tend to make better decisions, are more likely to achieve their goals, have more satisfying relationships, and basically have a better life. People with troubled brains, however, tend to struggle in all areas of their lives.

The brain is the most complicated, amazing, special organ in the universe. Your brain weighs only about three pounds, but it is more powerful than the most sophisticated supercomputer. Even though it represents only about 2 percent of your body's weight, your brain uses about 25 percent of the calories you consume, 25 percent of the total blood flow in your body, and 20 percent of the oxygen you breathe. The calories, blood flow, and oxygen feed the neurons (also called nerve cells or brain cells) inside your brain.

It is estimated that the brain contains more than 100 billion nerve cells, which is about the number of stars in the Milky Way. Each neuron is connected to other neurons via thousands of connections called synapses. There are more connections inside your head than there are stars in the universe! If you take a single piece of brain tissue the size of a grain of sand, it contains 100,000 nerve cells and a billion connections — all "talking" to each other.

When we do full-body scans, the brain is lit up like a little heater while the rest of the body appears ghostlike. This occurs because your brain is the command and control center of all activity in your body. Quite simply, the brain is what makes you who you are.

Imaging the brain gives us great insight into healing the brain. Many of us are walking around with brains that could use some serious help, but because we cannot see our brains, we do not realize there is a problem, and we do nothing to fix it.

As a psychiatrist, this really concerns me. Looking at the brain has made a huge difference in both my professional and personal life. At the time I ordered my first scan I had been a psychiatrist for nearly a decade, and I realized that I did not have all the information necessary to provide the very best treatment for my patients. Asking my patients to describe what was troubling them was not always enough to make a diagnosis or develop a treatment plan. When I scanned my first patient, I was excited to discover that I could see what was going on inside the brain. It did not take long for me to come to the conclusion that brain scans could help me be a better doctor.

The brain-imaging technology we use is called SPECT, which stands for single photon emission computed tomography. SPECT scans look at blood flow and activity patterns in the brain. Unlike MRI and CAT scans, which show the anatomy of the brain, SPECT scans look at brain function. SPECT scans reveal three things about the brain: areas that are working well, areas that are working too hard, and areas that are not working hard enough.

Since 1991, I have studied more than 55,000 brain scans. Analyzing scans has helped me to better diagnose and treat my patients for a variety of problems, such as ADD, depression, anxiety, anger, and addictions. In addition, I have discovered that by improving your brain function, I could help you improve your life.

You can change your brain and enhance your life! The best thing about your brain is that it can change. Even if you have not been treating your brain with TLC, you can make it better! By avoiding bad brain habits and adopting as many good brain habits as possible, you can improve brain function and improve your life, family, career, business, school, and health.

List one way the health or trouble in your brain has affected each of the following areas in your life.

Health _____

_____

Work _____

_____

Relationships _____

_____

Finances _____

_____

Past _____

_____

Present _____

_____

Future _____

_____

Three Ways to Enhance Your Emotional Relationship With Your Brain

1. Talk about the brain with family members, friends, coworkers, and classmates.

2. Look for articles and features about the brain in newspapers, magazines, and on TV. You will quickly discover that nearly every story you see involves the brain in some way.

3. Use *Dr. Amen's Change Your Brain, Change Your Body Daily Journal* to help you focus on brain health and track your progress.

Case Study: Dr. Amen at Age 37 and Age 52

I know from first-hand experience just how harmful bad brain habits can be. I had my first brain scan at age 37, and it was not the picture of health. I couldn't understand why. I rarely drank alcohol, and I had never taken illegal drugs, so why did my brain look so bad? I didn't know it at the time, but many of my daily habits were contributing to the problem. I practically lived on fast food and diet sodas filled with aspartame. I worked like a nut, rarely got more than five hours of sleep at night and seldom found the time to exercise. Plus, my marriage at the time was filled with chronic stress and conflict. I was guilty of having a lot of bad brain habits.

Dr. Amen's Brain at Age 37   Dr. Amen's Brain at Age 52

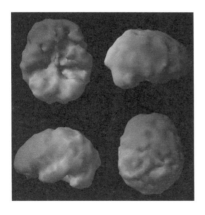 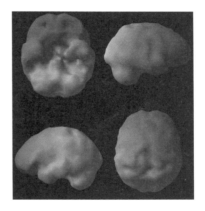

Seeing my own SPECT scan gave me "brain envy." I wanted a better brain, so I changed my behavior. I learned more about brain health and started living a brain healthy life, and it worked. My last scan at age 52 looked healthier and much younger than my scan at age 37, which is not usually what happens. Typically brains get less active with age, not more active.

Know Your Brain

ONE SIZE DOES NOT FIT EVERYONE — TARGETED INTERVENTIONS JUST FOR YOU

One prescription does not fit everyone. This is why so many self-help programs and diets do not work. All of us need individualized or personalized prescriptions based on our own brain types and needs. First, it is important to become familiar with the brain systems that play a major role in your ability to get a life, a career, a relationship, a family, and a body you love. All of these systems can influence your behavior and either help or hurt your ability to be your best.

Outside View of the Brain

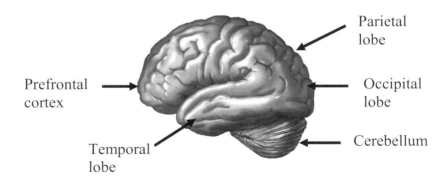

Inside View of the Brain

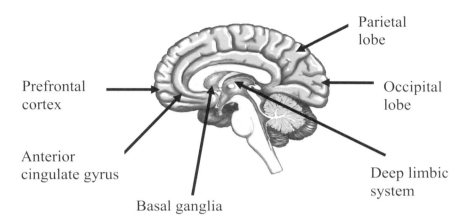

Prefrontal cortex

Parietal lobe

Occipital lobe

Anterior cingulate gyrus

Deep limbic system

Basal ganglia

Prefrontal Cortex (PFC)

Think of the PFC as the CEO of your brain. Situated at the front third of your brain, it acts like a supervisor for the rest of your brain and body. It is the brain's brake that helps you think about what you say and do before you say or do it. It is involved with attention, judgment, planning, impulse control, follow-through, and empathy.

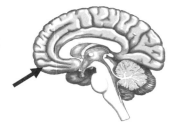

- At work, the PFC helps you plan your day effectively and finish your projects on time.
- In your relationships, the PFC makes you think twice before saying something hurtful to your significant other.
- The PFC tells you to keep walking when you pass by the Cinnabon store at the mall.
- At school, the PFC helps kids pay attention to their teachers and helps teachers listen to their students.

When the PFC is low in activity, often due to low levels of the neurotransmitter dopamine or brain trauma, people often struggle with:

- Impulse control problems
- Distractibility
- Lack of clear focus or goals
- Procrastination
- Disinhibition
- Impulsive overeating
- Short attention span
- Decreased forethought
- Decreased judgment
- Financial problems

Having low PFC activity may have some positive traits, such as:

- Spontaneous
- Not rule bound
- Creative
- Uninhibited free spirit
- Can be a great salesperson

Some conditions associated with low PFC activity include:

- ADHD
- Brain trauma
- Some forms of depression

Common treatments used when the PFC is low:

- Organizational help
- Intense aerobic exercise, see Step 6

For ADHD:

- Supplements such as *Dr. Daniel Amen's Nutraceutical Solutions: Focus & Energy Optimizer* or *Dr. Daniel Amen's Nutraceutical Solutions: Attention Support: Children & Teens*
- Medications such as Adderall, Ritalin, or Stratterra

For Depression:

- Supplements such as *Dr. Daniel Amen's Nutraceutical Solutions: SAMe Mood & Movement Support*
- Medications such as Wellbutrin

Anterior Cingulate Gyrus (ACG)

The ACG is like the brain's gear shifter. It runs lengthwise through the deep parts of the frontal lobes and allows us to shift our attention and be flexible and adaptable and to change when needed.

- In the office, the ACG allows you to shift directions when the boss asks you to drop what you're working on and tackle another project instead.
- A healthy ACG helps everyone at home go with the flow so you have a peaceful family life.
- The ACG helps teachers and students shift their attention from one class to the next throughout the school day.
- Your ACG helps you see options when faced with obstacles that could derail your diet or exercise plan.

When the ACG is high in activity, often due to low levels of the neurotransmitter serotonin, people often struggle with:

- Trouble shifting their attention
- Tendency to worry
- Argumentative with family members
- Obsessive thoughts
- Compulsive overeating
- Compulsive behaviors
- Oppose new ideas/strategies at work
- Get stuck on negative thoughts or actions
- Hold grudges against loved ones/coworkers

Having high ACG activity may have some positive traits, such as:

- Very focused
- Goal-oriented
- Very organized
- Stay on track
- Predictable
- Can be a great accountant or number-cruncher

Some medical conditions associated with high ACG activity include:

- Obsessive compulsive disorder
- PMS
- Chronic pain
- Posttraumatic stress disorder
- Anxiety disorders, get stuck on negative thoughts
- Eating disorders, such as compulsive overeating

Common treatments used when the ACG is high:

- Distraction, paradox, options Boost serotonin:
- Intense aerobic exercise, see Step 6
- Supplements such as *Dr. Daniel Amen's Nutraceutical Solutions: Serotonin Mood Support*
- Medications such as SSRIs (Prozac, Zoloft, Lexapro, etc.)

Deep Limbic System (DLS)

Lying near the center of the brain, the deep limbic system is involved in setting a person's emotional tone. When the activity in this area is normal, people tend to be more positive and hopeful.

- The DLS increases your motivation to succeed at work.
- A healthy DLS promotes stable moods that help keep your home life calm.
- When the DLS works right, it makes it easier for teachers to bond with their students.
- Normal activity in the DLS makes you less likely to engage in emotional overeating.

When the DLS is high in activity, often due to low levels of different neurotransmitters, such as serotonin, dopamine, or norepinephrine, people often struggle with:

- Negativity
- Decreased self-esteem
- Sadness
- Trouble sleeping
- Guilt
- SAD overeating
- Lowered motivation and drive
- Mood disorders, such as depression
- Lack of energy
- Appetite changes
- Feelings of hopelessness or worthlessness

Having high DLS activity may have some positive traits, such as:

- Increased empathy for people who suffer
- More in touch with feelings

Some medical conditions associated with high DLS activity include:

- Depression
- Dysthymia (chronic, mild depression)
- Cyclic mood disorders
- Pain syndromes

Common treatments used when the DLS is high:

- Intense aerobic exercise, see Step 6
- Learning to kill ANTs, see Step 9

For Depression:
- Supplements such as *Dr. Daniel Amen's Nutraceutical Solutions: SAMe Mood & Movement Support*
- Medications such as Wellbutrin

For Pain:
- Supplements such as fish oil *Dr. Daniel Amen's Nutraceutical Solutions: Omega-3 Power*, plus *Dr. Daniel Amen's Nutraceutical Solutions: SAMe Mood & Movement Support*

Basal Ganglia (BG)

Surrounding the deep limbic system, the basal ganglia are involved with integrating thoughts, feelings, and movements. This part of the brain is involved in setting a person's anxiety level. This area is also involved with feelings of pleasure and ecstasy. Cocaine works in this part of the brain. Cookies, cakes, and other treats also activate this area, according to a new book called *The End of Overeating* by Dr. David Kessler, the former commissioner of the U.S. Food and Drug Administration.

- With normal activity in this area, you can handle extra pressure at work without getting completely stressed out.
- When the basal ganglia are well-balanced, it helps keep you from worrying excessively about your children.
- Teachers who have normal activity here are better able to keep calm in the classroom.
- Healthy basal ganglia can help keep you from bingeing on sweets or abusing alcohol or drugs to calm yourself down.

When the BG is high in activity, often due to low levels of the neurotransmitter GABA, people often struggle with:

- Anxiety
- Panic
- Predicting the worst
- Excessive stress
- Conflict avoidant
- Muscle tension
- Nervousness
- Anxious overeating
- Physical stress symptoms, (headache, stomachache)

Having high BG activity may have some positive traits, such as:

- Increased motivation
- Conscientiousness
- Self-discipline
- Ability/desire to work for long periods

Some medical conditions associated with high BG activity include:

- Physical stress disorders, (headaches, GI problems)
- Anxiety disorders

Common treatments used when the BG are too high:

- Body biofeedback
- Relaxing music
- Limit caffeine/alcohol
- Hypnosis, meditation
- Learning to kill ANTs, see Step 9
- Intense aerobic exercise, see Step 6
- Assertiveness training

For Anxiety:
- Supplements such as *Dr. Daniel Amen's Nutraceutical Solutions: GABA Calming Support*
- Medications such as BuSpar or Neurontin

Temporal Lobes (TLs)

The temporal lobes, located underneath your temples and behind your eyes, are involved with language, memory, mood stability, and temper issues. They are part of the brain's "What Pathway," because they help you recognize and name "what" things are. Temporal lobe problems can lead to angry outbursts and 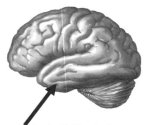 confrontations. Abnormal activity in this area can also make it difficult for you to learn new things or remember important things, like your wedding anniversary or when to take your supplements or medication — these can be detrimental to your relationships and health.

- At work, the temporal lobes help you read social cues, such as understanding when it is or isn't a good time to approach the boss to discuss your promotion.
- When the temporal lobes work right, it keeps you from yelling and screaming at your kids when you get frustrated.
- This area of the brain helps students with listening and reading.
- The temporal lobes help you remember all the things you need to do to stay healthy.

When the TLs are abnormal in activity, often due to low levels of the neurotransmitters GABA or acetylcholine, people often struggle with:

- Memory problems
- Irritability
- Anxiety for no clear reason
- Trouble finding words
- Poor reading
- Mood instability
- Temper problems
- Dark thoughts
- Processing problems
- Trouble reading social cues

Some medical conditions associated with abnormal TL activity include:

- Head injury
- Epilepsy
- Amnesia
- Anxiety
- Dementia

Common treatments used when the BG are too high:

For mood instability and irritability:
- Supplements such as *Dr. Daniel Amen's Nutraceutical Solutions: GABA Calming Support*
- Medications — anti-seizure medications such as Neurontin, Depakote, or Lamictal

For memory problems:
- Supplements such as *Dr. Daniel Amen's Nutraceutical Solutions: Brain & Memory Power Boost*
- Medications — memory enhancers such as Aricept or Namenda

Cerebellum (CB)

The cerebellum, at the back bottom part of the brain, is called the little brain. Even though it represents only 10 percent of the brain's volume, it houses 50 percent of the brain's neurons. It is usually the most active part of the brain and is usually symmetrical in appearance. The cerebellum is involved with motor coordination, posture, and how we walk. It is also involved with processing speed, like clock speed on a computer. It is also involved with thought coordination, or how quickly you can make cognitive and emotional adjustments.

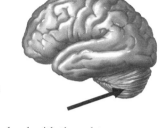

- At work, a healthy cerebellum is one of the keys to being a good problem-solver.
- When working optimally, the cerebellum improves athletic performance.
- In school, the cerebellum helps you think quickly, which facilitates test-taking.
- Family life and relationships are generally smoother with good activity in the cerebellum.

When the CB is low in activity people often struggle with:
- Poor physical coordination
- Poor judgment
- Impulsivity
- Disorganization
- Slowed thinking
- Trouble learning

Common treatments used when the CB is low in activity:
- Interactive Metronome
- Brain Gym Exercises
- Coordination exercises, such as dancing, table tennis
- Video game Dance Dance Revolution

There are no clear supplements or medications known to enhance cerebellar activity.

How the Brain Systems Influence Who You Are

To show how your brain plays the most vital role in your ability to have a great life, a satisfying career, success in school, wonderful relationships, and a body you love, let's take a look at some common examples of how these brain systems play out in everyday life.

1. **Fathers who are strict and have very rigid rules:** Fathers who are extremely rigid tend to have excessive activity in the ACG. When there is increased activity in this area, it makes fathers likely to use phrases like, "It's my way or the highway."

2. **People who are impulsive:** I once treated a 42-year-old woman who failed six alcohol treatment programs. Her impulse control was virtually zero. It turned out that she had been kicked in the head by a horse when she was 10 years old. Her brain SPECT scan showed severe damage to the prefrontal cortex. She had virtually no supervisor in her head. If I did not address the damaged PFC, she would never be well. Giving her treatment to enhance PFC function was very helpful to her.

3. **People who are compulsive overeaters:** Rebecca, 44, couldn't stop thinking about food and had gained 80 pounds despite trying many diets. The Atkins diet — a very high-protein, low-carbohydrate diet — made her irritable and emotional. Diet pills made her anxious. Her brain SPECT study showed too much activity in the ACG, likely due to low levels of the neurotransmitter serotonin. On a rational weight-loss program plus a regimen of 5-HTP to boost serotonin levels in her brain, she lost weight, felt much happier overall, was more relaxed, and got along better with her husband.

4. **Employees who are anxious and constantly predicting why things won't work:** Individuals who focus on fear and the negative tend to have overactivity in the basal ganglia. Low levels of the neurotransmitter GABA are often at the root of these self-defeating attitudes. Taking supplements to boost GABA may help.

5. **Bosses who get angry and scream when they run into problems:** These people tend to have too little activity in the temporal lobes, the part of the brain that is responsible for temper control. GABA supplements can calm anger while ginkgo biloba and Huperzine A can improve memory.

6. **Students who are usually on time, do what they promise, have a positive attitude, and are well-liked by others:** These traits are usually the signs of a balanced and healthy brain.

Knowing how your own specific brain works is critical to getting the help that will work for you. Of course, as you will see, there are interventions that apply to all of us, such as eating a brain healthy diet and getting adequate sleep, but to get the best out of this program, pay attention to the individual types of interventions that may apply to you.

Why would a doctor NEVER give a patient the diagnosis of chest pain? Because it is a symptom. It is too broad, and it has far too many causes to be considered a diagnosis or a single entity. What can cause chest pain? Many problems that range from the top of your head all the way to your pelvis, such as grief, panic attacks, hyperthyroidism, pneumonia, lung cancer, toxic exposure, a heart attack, abnormal heart rhythm, heart infection, rib injuries, indigestion, gastric reflux esophagitis, gallbladder stones, liver disease, kidney disease, and pancreatic cancer. Chest pain has many different possible causes and many possible treatments.

In the same way, what can cause obesity? Again, many different problems such as a poor diet, no exercise, low thyroid, pituitary tumors, certain forms of depression, and some medications. Obesity can be caused by low activity in the PFC, causing people to eat impulsively, or by increased BG activity, causing people to be anxious overeaters. Obesity can be caused by increased ACG activity (the obsessive sort of obesity) or by increased DLS activity (the emotional kind of overeating) or a combination of these, plus still other problems. There are many different types of obesity.

How does chest pain relate to obesity, skin problems, low energy, or depression? All of these problems are based on symptoms, not causes. As such, many physicians and patients view these common problems as single or simple disorders. Since they view these disorders in a simplistic way, they often have the idea that one treatment fits everyone with a certain disorder. From a brain-imaging perspective this attitude just does not make sense, as there is not one type of obesity, stress response, anxiety, or depression.

Understanding your individual brain is critical to getting the right help, whether it is to help your mood, your focus, your weight, or your overall health. This is one of the reasons why being honest and forthright on Dr. Amen's Change Your Brain, Change Your Body Questionnaire is critical to the success of your program.

My Results from Dr. Amen's Change Your Brain, Change Your Body Questionnaire

Place a checkmark next to the areas where your brain may need help:

- ☐ Prefrontal cortex (PFC)
- ☐ Anterior cingulate gyrus (ACG)
- ☐ Deep limbic system (DLS)
- ☐ Basal ganglia (BG)
- ☐ Temporal lobes (TL)
- ☐ Memory problems
- ☐ Cerebellum (CB)
- ☐ Insomnia
- ☐ Sleep apnea
- ☐ Hypoglycemia
- ☐ Scotopic sensitivity syndrome
- ☐ Cravings
- ☐ Seasonal mood disorder
- ☐ Bad brain habits
- ☐ Compulsive overeating
- ☐ Impulsive overeating
- ☐ Impulsive-compulsive overeating
- ☐ SAD or emotional overeating
- ☐ Anxious overeating
- ☐ Low energy
- ☐ Chronic pain
- ☐ Brain recovery
- ☐ Bipolar
- ☐ Taking blood thinners

Five Types of Obesity

Through our brain-imaging work I have discovered five different types of overeaters, based on brain systems. Here is a summary.

TYPE 1: COMPULSIVE OVEREATERS

People with this type have trouble shifting their attention and tend to get stuck on thoughts of food or compulsive eating behaviors. They may also get stuck on anxious or depressing thoughts. The basic mechanism of this type is that they tend to get stuck or locked into one course of action. They tend to have trouble seeing options and want to have things their way. They struggle with cognitive inflexibility. This type is also associated with worry, holding grudges, and having problems with oppositional or argumentative behavior. Nighttime-eating syndrome, where people tend to gorge at night and not be hungry early in the day, usually fits this pattern.

The most common brain SPECT finding in this type is increased anterior cingulate gyrus activity, which is most commonly caused by low brain serotonin levels. High-protein diets, diet pills, and stimulants, such as Ritalin, usually make this type worse. Interventions to boost serotonin in the brain are generally the most helpful. From a supplement standpoint 5-HTP, L-tryptophan, St. John's wort, the B vitamin inositol, and the saffron extract satiereal are helpful, as are the serotonin-enhancing medications, such as Prozac, Zoloft, and Lexapro. 5-HTP, in fact, has good scientific evidence that it helps with weight loss, and in my experience it works best for this type.

Behavioral interventions that boost serotonin to help compulsive overeaters:

- Exercise to allow more of the serotonin precursor l-tryptophan to get into the brain.
- If you get a thought in your head more than three times, get up and go do something to distract yourself.

- Have several options because people with this type always do better with choices, rather than edicts.
- Avoid automatically opposing others or saying no, even to yourself.
- If you have trouble sleeping, try a glass of warm milk with a teaspoon of vanilla and a few drops of stevia.

TYPE 2: IMPULSIVE OVEREATERS

People with this type struggle with impulsivity and trouble controlling their behavior, even though nearly every day they intend to eat well. "I am going to start my diet tomorrow," is their common mantra. This type results from too little activity in the brain's PFC. The PFC acts as the brain's supervisor. It helps with executive functions, such as attention span, forethought, impulse control, organization, motivation, and planning. When the PFC is underactive, people complain of being inattentive, distracted, bored, off task, and impulsive. This type is often seen in conjunction with ADD, which is associated with longstanding issues of short attention span, distractibility, disorganization, restlessness, and impulsivity.

Research published in the July 2008 issue of *Pediatrics* found that children and adolescents with ADD who do not currently take medications are at increased risk for being overweight. Data on almost 63,000 children and adolescents, ages 5 to 17, was collected. Subjects were classified as underweight, normal weight, at risk of overweight, or overweight according to body mass index (BMI) for age and gender. Researchers from Brown Medical School found that ADD children not currently using medication were at 1.5 times the risk of being overweight than non-ADD children. These individuals are more likely to be impulsive overeaters. On the other hand, those taking medication for ADD had 1.6 times more risk of being underweight compared to children without ADD, which is a side effect of their medication, which decreases appetite.

Impulsive overeaters may also be the result of some form of toxic exposure, a near-drowning accident, a brain injury to the front part of the brain, or a brain infection, such as chronic fatigue syndrome. The most common brain SPECT finding in this type is decreased activity in the PFC, which is most commonly associated with low brain dopamine levels. High-carbohydrate diets and serotonin-enhancing medications, such as Prozac, Zoloft, or Lexapro, or supplements, such as 5-HTP, usually make this type worse. Interventions to boost dopamine in the brain are generally the most helpful. From a supplement standpoint, green tea and rhodiola are helpful, as are stimulant medications, such as phentermine or Adderall and Ritalin, which are commonly used to treat ADD.

Behavioral interventions that boost dopamine to help impulsive overeaters:

- Exercise, which helps increase blood flow and dopamine in the brain— especially, doing an exercise you love.
- Clear focus — make a list of weight and health goals and put it where you can see it everyday.
- Outside supervision — have someone you trust check in with you on a regular basis to help you stay focused.
- Avoid impulsively saying yes to offers for more food or drink and practice saying, "No, thank you, I'm full."

TYPE 3: IMPULSIVE-COMPULSIVE OVEREATERS

People with this type have a combination of both impulsive and compulsive features. The brain SPECT scans tend to show low activity in the PFC (associated with impulsivity, likely due to low dopamine levels) and high activity in the anterior cingulate gyrus (associated with compulsivity and low serotonin levels). This pattern is common in the children or grandchildren of alcoholics. People with this mixed type tend to have done very well emotionally and behaviorally on the fen-phen combination, which raised both dopamine and serotonin in the brain.

Using serotonin or dopamine interventions by themselves usually makes the problem worse. For example, using a serotonin medication or supplement helps to calm the compulsions but makes the impulsivity worse. Using a dopamine medication or supplement helps to lessen the impulsivity but increases the compulsive behaviors. Treatments to raise dopamine and serotonin together, with either a combination of supplements, such as green tea and 5-HTP, or medications, such as Prozac and Ritalin, have worked the best in my experience.

Behavioral interventions that boost both serotonin and dopamine to help impulsive-compulsive overeaters:

- Exercise.
- Set goals.
- Avoid automatically opposing others or saying no, even to yourself.
- Avoid impulsively saying yes.
- Have options.
- Distract yourself if you get a thought stuck in your head.

TYPE 4: SAD OR EMOTIONAL OVEREATERS

People with this type often eat to medicate underlying feelings of boredom, loneliness, or depression. Their symptoms can range from winter blues, mild chronic sadness (termed dysthymia) to more serious depressions. Other symptoms may include a loss of interest in usually pleasurable activities; decreased libido; periods of crying; feelings of guilt, helplessness, hopelessness, or worthlessness; sleep and appetite changes; low energy levels; suicidal thoughts; and low self-esteem. The SPECT findings that correlate with this type are markedly increased activity in the deep limbic areas of the brain and decreased PFC activity.

When this type occurs in the winter, it is usually in more northern climates, where there is often a deficiency in sunlight and vitamin D levels. Low vitamin D levels have been associated with depression, memory problems, obesity, heart disease, and immune suppression. In recent years, there is an increase in vitamin D deficiencies even in southern and western states in the summer. There are two reasons for this: people are wearing sunscreen more than ever, so they are not being exposed to the sun even when they are outside, and they are spending more and more time indoors on their computers or watching TV. Some researchers believe nearly half of the U.S. population suffers from a vitamin D deficiency. I screen all of my patients for it by ordering a 25-hydroxy vitamin D level. To treat SAD or emotional overeaters, check vitamin D levels and correct them when low. Bright light therapy may be helpful to correct vitamin D problems, help with mood states, and help people lose weight.

There is evidence that bright light therapy might enhance the effectiveness of physical activity for weight loss. It significantly reduced the binge-eating episodes in people with bulimia and is an effective treatment for SAD, and has even been shown to be more effective than Prozac for these patients. Using bright light therapy in the workplace was effective in improving mood, energy, alertness, and productivity.

Also, make sure to check your DHEA blood levels. DHEA is a master hormone that has been found to be low in many people with depression and obesity. Supplementing with DHEA has good scientific evidence that it is helpful for weight loss in certain patients. Another helpful treatment for emotional overeaters is the natural supplement SAMe, in dosages of 400 to 1,600 mg. Be careful with SAMe if you have ever experienced a manic episode and take it early in the day as it has energizing properties and may interfere with sleep. I like the medication Wellbutrin for this type, which has been shown to have weight-reducing properties.

Behavioral interventions that boost mood to help SAD or emotional overeaters:

- Exercise to increase blood flow and multiple neurotransmitters in the brain.
- Kill the ANTs (automatic negative thoughts) that steal your

happiness.

- Write down five things you are grateful for everyday (this has been shown to increase your level of happiness in just three weeks).
- Volunteer to help others, which helps to get you outside of yourself and less focused on your own internal problems.
- Surround yourself with great smells, such as lavender.
- Try melatonin to help you sleep.
- Work to improve your relationships.

TYPE 5: ANXIOUS OVEREATERS

People with this type tend to use food to medicate underlying feelings of anxiety, tension, nervousness, and fear. They tend to feel uncomfortable in their own skin. They may be plagued by feelings of panic, fear, and self-doubt, and suffer physical symptoms of anxiety as well, such as muscle tension, nail biting, headaches, abdominal pain, heart palpitations, shortness of breath, and sore muscles. It is as if they have an overload of tension and emotion.

People with this type tend to predict the worst and look to the future with fear. They may be excessively shy, easily startled, and freeze in emotionally charged situations. The SPECT finding in this type is increased activity in the basal ganglia, which is commonly caused by low levels of the calming neurotransmitter GABA. Interventions to boost GABA, by using B_6, magnesium, and GABA are generally the most helpful. From a medication standpoint, the anticonvulsant Topamax has strong evidence it is helpful for weight loss, and in my experience, it is especially helpful for this type. Relaxation therapies can also be helpful to calm this part of the brain.

Behavioral interventions that boost GABA and calm the brain to help anxious overeaters:

- Exercise.

- Try relaxation exercises, such as:
    - meditation
    - prayer
    - hypnosis
    - deep diaphragmatic breathing exercises
    - hand-warming techniques
- Kill the anxious ANTs.
- For sleep, try self-hypnosis, kava kava, or valerian root.

Knowing the type of overeater you are is critical to getting the right help.

STEP 3

Boost Your Brain's Reserve

THE MORE RESERVE YOU HAVE, THE EASIER IT IS TO STICK WITH A BRAIN HEALTHY PROGRAM

Think about your family, friends, students, and coworkers. When there's a crisis, do some of them completely fall apart — racing for the candy bowl, reaching for a pack of cigarettes, or searching for solace in drugs and alcohol — while others manage to soldier on with their lives in a healthy way? Have you ever wondered why that is? I have. In my work, I have noticed that stressful events, such as the loss of a loved one, layoffs at work, or divorce can lead to depression, changes in weight, a lack of motivation, and bad daily habits in some people but not in others.

Similarly, experiencing a mild head injury can seriously alter some people's lives but doesn't affect the lives of other people. These differences are also noticeable in far less dramatic situations. For example, some individuals can work or study for hours on end without a break, while others feel wiped out after a brief study session or just a few hours at work. After looking at brain scans for nearly 20 years, I have come to believe that it has to do with a concept I call "brain reserve."

What is brain reserve? Brain reserve is the cushion of healthy brain function we have to deal with stressful events or injuries. The more reserve you have, the better you can cope with the unexpected. The less you have, the harder it is for you to handle tough times and injuries, and the more likely you are to gobble up a bag of Oreo cookies, swig alcohol, or reach for a cigarette as a coping mechanism.

At conception, most of us have the same amount of brain reserve. From that point on, though, many things can boost or reduce our level of reserve.

Things That Reduce Brain Reserve

You may be surprised to find out that common, everyday activities and behaviors are often the source of brain drain. Here are some common things that can hurt your brain and lower your reserve. Some of these will be covered in greater detail later in this book.

PHYSICAL TRAUMA

After looking at more than 55,000 scans, I have learned that even mild physical trauma can damage the brain and limit your ability to be successful in some or all areas of your life. Mood problems, alcoholism, drug abuse, divorce, trouble with the law, domestic violence, and financial problems are all more common in people who have experienced head injuries. That is why we need to do a better job of protecting our brains.

Throughout my career, I have been trying to get people to understand how important it is to keep our brains safe. Many routine activities and popular recreational sports make us vulnerable to brain injuries, including the following.

Bicycling
Bike accidents are the number one cause of brain injuries among adults and children. In fact, biking, skateboarding, and skating accidents account for almost 50 percent of all head injuries sustained in recreational activities or sports, according to the American Academy of Pediatrics. If you must ride a bike, it is critical to wear a helmet that fits properly. Helmets that do not fit are not much protection at all.

Football
New research shows that football players who experience one or more concussions display impaired thinking skills and signs

of early dementia as they age. The Amen Clinics is conducting one of the largest brain-imaging studies to date on retired NFL players. After looking at their brain scans, I can assure you that playing tackle football is NOT good for your brain.

Boxing

I have scanned several champion boxers, and I can tell you that their brains are a mess. What else would you expect when you have spent your life taking repeated blows to the head? Boxers are susceptible to a particular form of severe brain injury called dementia pugilistica. This results in impaired mental and physical abilities, including dementia and Parkinson's disease.

Soccer

Did you know that soccer players have just as many concussions as football players? Research also shows that retired soccer players tend to have brain abnormalities due to repeatedly heading the ball and crashing into the goalposts, the ground, or other players. A 2004 study conducted by the Sporting Goods Manufacturers Association found that current and former soccer players performed worse than the general public on some types of IQ tests. Not only that, 81 percent of the former players tested had memory or concentration problems.

Driving

When it comes to driving, make sure you only get behind the wheel of safe vehicles. Skip the motorcycles and ATVs, and always wear your seatbelt!

DRUGS

Marijuana, cocaine, ecstasy, methamphetamines, inhalants, and heroin seriously decrease brain function and affect one's ability to succeed. Illegal drugs aren't the only culprits. Abusing prescription medications, such as Vicodin, Oxycontin, and Xanax, can also harm the brain. Oxycontin is currently the second most abused drug in the United States, and it can decrease overall brain function.

As a guest expert on Season Three of the VH1 show, *Celebrity Rehab* with Dr. Drew Pinsky, I was asked to do brain SPECT scans on three of the cast members: the troubled basketball star Dennis Rodman, country singer Mindy McCready, and ex-Hollywood Madam Heidi Fleiss. Heidi was on the show for problems with methamphetamines. At age 43, both Heidi and her brain looked much older than she was.

ALCOHOL

Alcohol is NOT a health food. In recent years, there has been a lot of research suggesting that drinking red wine is good for your heart. After viewing tens of thousands of brain scans, however, I have found that alcohol negatively affects the brain in a number of ways. It lowers overall blood flow and activity in the brain, which over time, diminishes memory and judgment. Drinking specifically lowers activity in the PFC, the area responsible for judgment, forethought, and planning, which is why people who get drunk often act so stupid.

Drinking large amounts of alcohol — four or more glasses of wine or the equivalent in hard liquor on a daily basis — raises the risk of dementia. One study found that people who drink three times a week have smaller brains than nondrinkers. When it comes to the brain, size matters!

POOR NUTRITION

Your body uses the food it consumes to renew and replenish all of its cells. You literally are what you eat. That means if you eat a lot of junk food, you will have a junk-food mind. According to studies, 91 percent of Americans do not eat at least five servings of fruits and vegetables a day, the minimum required to get the nutrition your brain needs.

CHRONIC STRESS

Demands in the workplace and in people's private lives can lead to chronic stress. When you feel stressed all the time, your body secretes hormones that not only kill cells in the memory centers of the brain but also expand your waistline.

SLEEP DEPRIVATION

If you get less than seven hours of sleep a night, you have lower overall brain function.

SMOKING

Nicotine is found in cigarettes, cigars, chewing tobacco, and nicotine patches, gums, and tablets. It causes blood vessels to constrict, which lowers blood flow to the brain, depriving it of the nutrients it needs and eventually causing overall lowered activity. Blood flow is important because it carries oxygen, sugar, vitamins, and nutrients to the brain, and it gets rid of toxins.

Anything that compromises blood flow to the brain also restricts blood flow to the vital organs, including the genitals. This explains why smokers tend to be more likely to experience erectile dysfunction than nonsmokers. Most people can tell if a person is a smoker because their skin looks prematurely aged. I can tell you that their brains look prematurely aged, too.

TOO MUCH CAFFEINE

Drinking too much caffeinated coffee, tea, sodas, or energy drinks restricts blood flow to the brain, dehydrates the brain, and fools the brain into thinking it does not need to sleep. These are all bad things for your brain.

DEHYDRATION

Your body consists of 70 percent water, and your brain is 80 percent water. If you aren't drinking enough water, you reduce brain function.

LACK OF EXERCISE

When you don't exercise, you decrease blood flow to the brain.

NEGATIVE THINKING

The Amen Clinics has conducted studies showing that focusing on the things you don't like lowers brain activity.

EXCESSIVE VIDEO GAME PLAYING, TV WATCHING, INTERNET, OR TEXTING

In his fascinating book *Thrilled to Death: How the Endless Pursuit of Pleasure Is Leaving Us Numb*, psychologist Archibald Hart warns that text messaging, email, video games, and television can overstimulate our pleasure centers. Our pleasure centers are part of the brain's reward system, which is one of the body's most important survival mechanisms. It drives us to seek out things like food and sex that give us pleasure — and keep us (and the human race) alive.

Our pleasure centers are located deep within the brain and operate on a chemical called dopamine. Whenever we do something enjoyable, it's like pressing a button in the brain to release a little bit of dopamine to make us feel pleasure. But if we push these pleasure buttons too often or too strong we reduce their effectiveness. Eventually, it takes more and more flavor, excitement, or stimulation to feel pleasure. The evolution of technology in our society is wearing out the brain's pleasure centers, and I believe it's having a very negative effect on our bodies.

Limit TV time

Studies have linked TV watching with an increased risk for ADD, depression, obesity, and Alzheimer's disease.

Cut down on video game playing time

With SPECT imaging, we see that video games work in the same area of the brain that lights up with cocaine and methamphetamine use. New research shows that people can actually become addicted to video games, and that excessive gaming increases the likelihood of ADD and weight gain.

Get a handle on high-tech communications

Cell phones, text messaging, Instant Messaging, email, chat rooms, and social networking are the latest must-have communication tools. What's ironic is that these very communication devices may actually be causing communication breakdown as well as a host of other brain-related problems that can impact your body. Reports indicate that they may be stunting real-life social skills and the ability to communicate face-to-face. The distractions of emails and text messages have been shown to lower your IQ. Set specific times to check your messaging systems and leave them alone the rest of the time.

Exposure to environmental toxins

After nearly 20 years of looking at brain scans, I have seen that toxins can seriously damage the brain. Environmental toxins — such as mold, pesticides, and heavy metals — that harm the brain have been detected in homes, offices, schools, hair and nail salons, and many other locations across the nation.

In my experience, I have found that brain scans of indoor painters show some of the highest levels of brain damage I have ever seen. If you are painting indoors, make sure you have great ventilation. A recent study reported that hairdressers had a higher than normal risk for Alzheimer's disease. Limit your visits to hair and nail salons that have ample ventilation.

Many Things Boost Brain Reserve

After years of analyzing brain scans and treating patients, I have discovered that there are many simple things you can do on a daily basis to help your brain and boost your reserve. With a better brain, you are more likely to achieve all the things you have always wanted in life: a successful career, a growing business, a better body, improved health, and loving relationships.

The rest of this book will be focused on the things you can do to enhance brain function and increase reserve. Here is a preview of some of the best brain habits that will be discussed.

- Eat a brain healthy diet.
- Take a daily multiple vitamin and fish oil.
- Exercise.
- Get good sleep.
- Engage in new learning.
- Try positive thinking.
- Meditate.
- Use relaxation techniques.
- Increase your motivation.
- Surround yourself with loving relationships.
- Take control of your own brain health.

When you have ample brain reserve, it builds up your resilience and makes it easier for you to deal with life's unexpected twists and turns without turning to Ben & Jerry's ice cream, alcohol, or drugs.

On the following page, list out your behaviors and activities that are either hurting or enhancing your brain reserve, and then share it with someone. This will help keep you accountable to accomplish the goal. Email or call the other person to encourage you in the positive steps you are taking.

List your behaviors and activities that hurt your brain's reserve.

_____

_____

_____

_____

_____

_____

List your behaviors and activities that enhance your brain's reserve.

_____

_____

_____

_____

_____

_____

List the behaviors and activities you are willing to change to help your brain's reserve.

_____

_____

_____

_____

_____

_____

Case Study: Mary and Katie

Mary and Katie are identical twins. They share the same genes, the same parents, and the same upbringing. Yet their lives — and looks — are very different. Mary, who is very fit, is a successful journalist in a long-term happy marriage with three great children. Katie, who is overweight, barely finished high school, suffers with depression and a bad temper, and goes from job to job and relationship to relationship. Their lives and looks are nothing alike.

Mary's Healthy
SPECT Scan

Katie's Brain-Damaged
SPECT Scan

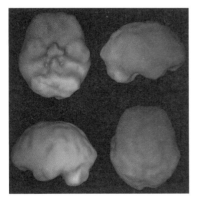 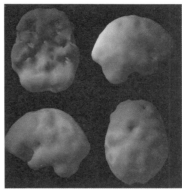

When I scanned them, Mary had a very healthy brain, while Katie had clear evidence of a brain injury, affecting her prefrontal cortex and temporal lobes. At first, when I talked with the twins together, Katie didn't remember a head injury. Then Mary spoke up saying, "Don't you remember the time when we were 10 years old and you fell off the top bunk bed onto your head? You got knocked out and we had to rush you to the hospital." The injury likely caused Katie to have less brain reserve, which may be why she was always more vulnerable to stress than her sister.

STEP 4

Nourish Your Brain

A BRAIN HEALTHY DIET AND SUPPLEMENTS FUELS YOUR BODY FOR BETTER HEALTH

When I was writing this book, I saw a feature on ESPN about Los Angeles Lakers forward Lamar Odom who has a terrible sweet tooth and consumes up to $80 worth of candy a week. As a Lakers season ticket holder, I have suffered through years of Odom's erratic performance. He is unbelievably talented, but often acts like a space cadet during games. I decided to write a piece for my blog (www.amenclinics.com/blog), which was picked up by the *Los Angeles Times*, which subsequently, caused a firestorm of controversy during the 2009 NBA finals.

In it, I wrote that Odom's candy addiction is bad news for the Lakers. Why? Sugar acts like a drug in the brain. It causes blood sugar levels to spike and then crash, leaving you feeling tired, irritable, foggy, and stupid. Eating too much sugar impairs cognitive function. Excessive sugar consumption also promotes inflammation, which can make your joints ache. It is also linked to headaches, mood swings, and weight gain. If Odom wants to be a world-class athlete who performs consistently, he needs to get his sugar consumption under control and eat a brain healthy diet.

If you want to look your best and perform your best at work, in relationships, or in school, you do, too. Eating right is one of the easiest, most effective strategies to improve the success of your family, business, or school. With nutritious foods, everybody — mom, dad, teens, toddlers, employees, managers, students, and teachers — will feel better, have more energy, and be mentally sharper, which is a recipe for success in every area of life.

Here, you will discover four truths about the foods you eat, and you will learn ten rules for brain healthy nutrition.

Four Truths About the Foods You Eat

Truth 1: You Literally Are What You Eat

Throughout your lifetime, all the cells in your body, including your brain cells, make themselves new every few months. Your skin cells are on an even faster turnaround, making themselves new every 30 days for as long as you live. Fueling this amazing cell regeneration are the foods you eat. If you want a healthy brain and body, proper nutrition is the key. I often say if you have a fast-food diet, you have a fast-food brain, and an overweight body.

Truth 2: Food Is A Drug

You have probably noticed how the foods you eat affect your mood and energy level. Or maybe you have noticed that every time your children snack on candy or cookies, they start bouncing off the walls. Or that when your boss guzzles coffee, she gets impatient and demanding. That is because food is a drug.

- **Food can make you feel worse.** If you chow down on three doughnuts for breakfast, about half an hour later, you are going to feel foggy, spacey, and stupid.

- **Food can make you sleepy.** Have you ever noticed that after wolfing down a huge lunch, you feel like you need a nap?

- **Food can make you feel great.** Eating the right foods gives you good energy that lasts all day long and helps you focus better.

Truth 3: Diet Influences Everything In Your Life

Food does a lot more than just alleviate hunger pangs. It affects every aspect of your physical health and well-being, including:

- **Your overall health.** Eat a poor diet, and your health will suffer. Nosh on nutrient-rich foods throughout the day, and you will have a stronger immune system.

- **Your ability to think quickly and clearly.** Brain-friendly foods rev up mental sharpness to help you stay focused on your goals.

- **Your performance at school and work.** A healthy diet gives you what you need to succeed.

- **Your relationships.** When your diet makes you feel good, it's easier to be good to those around you, and that makes everyone in the family, at work, and at school happier.

- **Your energy level.** Whether you are feeling peppy or pooped out depends on the foods you consume.

- **Your physical and athletic performance.** Good foods get you pumped up for physical activity while bad foods zap your stamina.

- **Your weight.** Your eating habits directly affect the size of your body.

- **Your appearance.** People who have healthy diets tend to look healthier.

Truth 4: Poor Eating Habits Are Making Us One Of The Fattest Nations

One-third of adult men and more than 35 percent of adult women in the U.S. are obese, and millions more are overweight. Obesity takes a toll on the health of our brains, bodies, families, businesses, and schools.

- Obesity has been linked to reduced cognitive ability in adults and children, depression, decreased self-esteem, and increased suicide attempts.

- Morbid obesity (at least 100 pounds overweight) is associated with more than 30 medical conditions and diseases, including type 2 diabetes, heart disease, and high blood pressure, as well as brain-related conditions, such as stroke, chronic headaches, and sleep apnea.

- Obesity costs the U.S. health care system up to $147 billion a year — an additional $1,429 for each obese person each year.

- Lost productivity, health care costs, and workers compensation costs due to physical inactivity, obesity, and overweight cost businesses in California alone nearly $22 billion in 2000.

10 Rules For Brain Healthy Nutrition

Rule 1: Get Adequate Hydration

Considering that your body consists of 70 percent water, and your brain is 80 percent water, proper hydration is the first rule of good nutrition. Even slight dehydration increases the body's stress hormones. Over time, increased levels of stress hormones are associated with memory problems, obesity, wrinkled skin, irritability, and problems thinking clearly. To stay adequately hydrated, drink at least half your weight in ounces. So, if you are 150 pounds, you should drink 75 ounces a day.

Avoid caffeinated beverages and alcohol, which cause dehydration. This means avoiding the sodas in the vending machines at work or school, saying no to the coffee pot in the employee break room, and skipping happy hour with coworkers.

Rule 2: Watch Your Calories

Eating less helps you live longer and is helpful for the brain and body, according to research. Not only that, reducing consumption controls weight and decreases the risk for heart disease, cancer, and stroke from obesity (a major risk factor for all these illnesses). Even better, restricting calories triggers certain mechanisms in the body to increase the production of nerve growth factors, which are beneficial to the brain.

To get the most out of low-calorie dining, eat with the acronym CRON (calorie restriction with optimal nutrition) in mind. That means making sure that every calorie you consume counts. Eating two doughnuts in the employee lounge for breakfast and then skipping lunch doesn't cut it.

Rule 3: Increase Good Fats & Decrease Bad Fats

Include more mono-unsaturated fats (found in avocados, olive oil, canola oil, peanut oil, and nuts) and polyunsaturated fats (found in safflower oil, corn oil, salmon, and mackerel) in your diet and limit or eliminate saturated fats (found in red meat, eggs, and dairy foods like whole milk and butter) and trans fats (found in store-bought cakes, crackers, cookies, potato chips, and margarine).

The Best Antioxidant Fruits & Vegetables
- *Acai berries*
- *Avocados*
- *Beets*
- *Blackberries*
- *Blueberries*
- *Broccoli*
- *Brussels sprouts*
- *Cherries*
- *Cranberries*
- *Kiwis*
- *Oranges*
- *Plums*
- *Raspberries*
- *Red bell peppers*
- *Red grapes*
- *Spinach*
- *Strawberries*
Source: USDA

The polyunsaturated fats found in salmon and mackerel and the monounsaturated fats found in canola oil and soybean oil are high in essential fatty acids (EFAs) called omega-3 fatty acids. They are called *essential* fatty acids because our body needs them. The problem is most of us do not get enough of them through the foods we eat. I recommend that people eat one to two servings of fish a week, particularly fish like wild salmon (not farm-raised) that is high in omega-3 fatty acids.

Rule 4: Increase Good Carbs & Decrease Bad Carbs

Carbohydrates are a necessary part of a healthy diet as they provide the fuel your body needs to perform physical activity. Some carbs are better than others. Complex carbs, which include fruits, vegetables, beans, legumes, and whole grains, get a thumbs-up. These foods take longer to digest and are loaded with vitamins, minerals, and fiber that promote a good brain and healthy body. The carbs to avoid are simple carbs, such as table sugar, pastries, candy, sodas, fruit juices, doughnuts, white bread, pasta, and white rice. Simple carbs are digested quickly, provide little or no nutritional value, and may promote disease and weight gain.

To help you figure out which carbs are high in sugar, check their glycemic index (GI) at www.glycemicindex.com. The GI rates carbs based on their effect on blood sugar levels. Low-glycemic carbs cause only small fluctuations in blood sugar levels, which help you maintain energy throughout the day. High-glycemic carbs cause blood sugar levels to spike and then crash. The key to good brain health is to make sure the majority of the carbs you consume are low-glycemic.

Rule 5: Replace Artificial Sweeteners With Natural Sweeteners

I used to drink gallons of diet soda. Then at age 35, I found that I had problems getting off the floor when I played with my young children because my joints hurt. Being a writer, I became even more concerned when my fingers and hands started to hurt as well.

As I became much more interested in learning about brain health, I discovered that there was a large body of information reporting that artificial sweeteners, like aspartame in diet sodas, may be associated with arthritis, gastrointestinal problems, headaches, memory problems, neurological problems, and a myriad of other maladies. I had a patient who told me her arthritis and headaches went away after she stopped aspartame. Another patient told me her confusion went away as she got rid of artificial sweeteners, and yet another patient told me that only after he stopped drinking diet sodas was he able to lose weight.

Rule 6: Take a Daily Multivitamin & Fish Oil Supplement

Ninety-one percent of Americans do not eat at least five servings of fruits and vegetables a day, the minimum required to get good nutrition. For years, I have been advocating that everybody take a daily multivitamin. The American Medical Association also now recommends a daily multivitamin for everybody because it helps prevent chronic illness.

In addition to a daily multivitamin, I often prescribe a fish oil supplement for my patients. Fish oil, a great source for omega-3 fatty acids, has been the focus of many scientific studies. Research has found that omega-3 fatty acid levels tend to be low in people with ADD, depression, and Alzheimer's disease, low in those who have trouble thinking, and low in those who attempt suicide. On the contrary, a diet rich in omega-3 fatty acids may promote a healthy emotional balance and positive mood, two things that will help the rest of your body.

Many other supplements can be beneficial for brain health. The specific supplements that are best for you depend on your needs based on your results from Dr. Amen's Change Your Brain, Change Your Body Questionnaire.

Rule 7: Balance the Foods You Eat

Your brain needs a balance of lean protein, such as skinless chicken or turkey, complex carbohydrates, and good fats. It is a good idea to include lean protein at each meal to balance blood sugar levels. Adding lean protein to snacks and meals slows the fast absorption of simple carbs and helps prevent the brain fog that typically follows consumption of sugary snacks.

Rule 8: Limit Caffeine Intake

If your caffeine intake is limited to one or two normal-size cups of coffee or tea a day, it probably is not a problem. But any more than that can spell trouble for your brain and body. Here are just five of the many reasons why.

- Caffeine restricts blood flow to the brain.
- Caffeine dehydrates the brain.
- Caffeine interferes with sleep.
- Caffeine is addictive.
- Caffeine can accelerate heart rate and raise blood pressure.

Rule 9: Reduce Salt Intake & Increase Potassium Intake

A lot of people erroneously blame salt for making them fat. Salt in and of itself does not cause weight gain, but it does cause your body to temporarily retain water, which can make it harder to zip up your jeans. Part of the problem with salt is that it is commonly found in large quantities in high-calorie processed foods at the grocery store, fast-food fare, and restaurant meals. So eating a diet that is high in high-salt foods is likely to make you gain weight over time.

Just as important as cutting back on salt is increasing potassium intake. Studies have found that eating twice as much potassium as sodium can cut the risk of dying from heart disease in half and that taking potassium supplements lowers blood pressure.

Foods high in potassium include bananas, spinach, honeydew melon, kiwi, lima beans, oranges, tomatoes, and all meats.

Rule 10: Eat Great Brain Foods

Foods that contain high amounts of antioxidants help your body and brain stay young. Several studies have found that eating antioxidants, which include many fruits and vegetables, significantly reduces the risk of developing cognitive impairment. Blueberries are very high in antioxidants, which has earned them the nickname "brainberries" among neuroscientists. Animal studies show that eating a diet rich in blueberries leads to reduced abdominal fat, lowered cholesterol, improved glucose levels, and a better ability to learn new motor skills.

Keeping a stash of antioxidant snacks in your desk at work or in your backpack at school can help you steer clear of the candy bowl on the teacher's desk or the birthday cake in the office kitchen.

The 50 Best Brain Foods

Almonds, raw
Almond milk, unsweetened
Apples
Asparagus
Avocados
Bananas
Beans (black, pinto, garbanzo)
Beets
Bell peppers (all colors)
Blackberries
Blueberries
Broccoli
Brussels sprouts
Carrots
Cheese, low fat
Cherries
Chicken, skinless
Cranberries
Egg whites, DHA enriched
Grapefruit
Herring
Honeydew
Kiwi
Lemons
Lentils

Limes
Oats
Olives
Olive oil
Oranges
Peaches
Peas
Plums
Pomegranates
Raspberries
Red grapes
Soybeans
Spinach
Strawberries
Tea, green
Tofu
Tomatoes
Tuna
Turkey, skinless
Walnuts
Water
Whole wheat
Wild salmon
Yams, sweet potatoes
Yogurt, unsweetened

My Top 20 Brain Foods
Make a list of your favorite brain foods and stock up on them.

1. _____
2. _____
3. _____
4. _____
5. _____
6. _____
7. _____
8. _____
9. _____
10. _____

11. _____
12. _____
13. _____
14. _____
15. _____
16. _____
17. _____
18. _____
19. _____
20. _____

What are the foods that you are saying "goodbye" to as you stock up on brain healthy foods?

_____

_____

_____

_____

_____

_____

_____

How did those foods make you feel? What did they do for you? What immediate action are you going to take? For example:

Ice cream makes me feel more alert and energizes me, then later I feel tired and sluggish. I will throw it away.

Chips calm me when I eat them in the evening. I will toss them, and NOT buy them at the store.

Brain Healthy Grocery Shopping Tips

1. Bring a list, and stick to it.

2. Don't shop when you are hungry!

3. Shop mainly on the outside aisles of the store. That is where you will find the produce, dairy, and meat and fish departments.

4. In the produce department, load up on spinach, broccoli, red peppers, oranges, lemons, and limes.

5. In the meat department, choose skinless chicken and turkey, wild salmon, and Ahi tuna.

6. In the dairy case, look for plain yogurt, soy milk, DHA-enriched eggs, Egg Beaters, and low-fat cheeses, such as mozzarella or string cheese.

7. In the deli case, choose lean meats, such as Canadian bacon.

8. In the frozen foods section, stick to the frozen fruits and vegetables.

9. Buy in bulk when possible.

10. Stay away from fruit juices. They are little more than liquid sugar.

11. Just say no to the candy and sodas at the checkout stand. They are impulse foods (geared to people with low frontal lobes).

12. Skip the junk food. There is no constitutional amendment that children have a right to junk food.

STEP 5

Rest Your Brain

GOOD SLEEP IS ESSENTIAL

You know how bad you look and feel after a night of poor sleep. You can barely muster the energy to get out of bed. You shuffle to the bathroom, turn on the light, and come face to face with puffy bags and dark circles under your eyes. You head out for your usual 30-minute jog but stop after 10 minutes because you feel whipped. Then you head to work where you snap at your coworkers and customers because you are in a foul mood.

Good sleep is essential for optimal brain and body health. It is involved in rejuvenating all the cells in your body, gives brain cells a chance to repair themselves, and activates neuronal connections that might otherwise deteriorate due to inactivity. It is also necessary if you want to have glowing skin, high energy, a sunny mood, excellent health, stable weight, and if you want to be successful at work or school. Unfortunately, as many as 70 million Americans have trouble sleeping. If you are one of them, your brain and body could be in trouble.

Average Number of Hours of Sleep Required By Age in Years

1-3 years	12-14 hours
3-5 years	11-13 hours
5-12 years	10-11 hours
13-19 years	9 hours
Adults	7-8 hours
Seniors	7-8 hours

Sources: National Sleep Foundation, National Institute of Neurological Disorders and Stroke

Sleep troubles come in many varieties. Do you have trouble falling asleep? Do you go to sleep easily but wake up repeatedly throughout the night? Do you find it hard to drag yourself out of bed in the morning? Do you or your significant other snore? All of these problems can lead to decreased brain function and a second-rate body. Getting less than six hours of sleep a night has been associated with lower overall brain activity, which can affect your weight, your skin, your mood, your health, your performance at work and at school, and your athletic performance.

Some of the many common causes of sleep deprivation include:

- Medication
- Too much caffeine
- Alcohol
- Nicotine
- Hormonal fluctuations
- Thyroid conditions
- Snoring
- Sleep apnea
- Stress
- Untreated or undertreated psychiatric conditions

Losing sleep can make you fat. An expanding body of evidence has shown that sleep deprivation is associated with weight gain and obesity. Numerous studies show that people who are sleep-deprived tend to eat more calories and are more likely to choose sugary treats and simple carbs, such as candy, cookies, and potato chips.

Sleep deprivation lowers brain function and impacts performance at work and school. People who get less than seven hours of sleep a night have lower activity in the temporal lobes, which are involved in memory and learning. This limits the ability to pay attention, learn, solve problems, and remember important information.

Lack of sleep hinders athletic performance. Research shows us that sleep deprivation impairs motor function, slows reaction times, and saps your energy.

Sleep deprivation worsens your mood. It should come as no surprise that being sleep deprived makes you more likely to be irritable and in an unpleasant mood. That spells trouble for your family, your coworkers, your students, or classmates.

Skimping on sleep leads to lifestyle habits that are bad for your brain. When you don't get enough sleep, you are inclined to gulp more caffeine, smoke more, exercise less, and drink more alcohol. Studies show that sleep-deprived adolescents are also more likely to drink alcohol, smoke marijuana, and use drugs than those who get enough sleep.

Poor sleep is linked to poor mental health. Scientific studies have shown a connection between sleep deprivation and depression, anxiety, ADD, and Alzheimer's disease.

Lack of sleep increases health risks. Sleep apnea significantly raises the risk of stroke, and thrashing around at night has been linked to a higher risk of developing Parkinson's disease.

10 Tips to Help You Go to Sleep and Stay Asleep

1. Maintain a regular sleep schedule — even on weekends.

2. Create a soothing nighttime routine (a warm bath, meditation, or massage).

3. Don't take daytime naps.

4. Listen to soothing music.

5. Engage in regular exercise — just not within four hours of bedtime.

6. Try self-hypnosis.

7. Turn off computers and cell phones two hours before bedtime.

8. Don't eat two to three hours before bedtime.

9. Avoid drinking caffeinated beverages in the late afternoon or evening.

10. Consider taking supplements, such as L-tryptophan, 5-HTP, valerian, kava kava, and melatonin.

If you have trouble sleeping, make copies of the following sleep journal and keep track of your sleeping habits.

MY SLEEP JOURNAL

Day/Date _____

Answer the following questions in the morning.

Last night, my bedtime ritual included: _____

_____

(List things like a warm bath, meditation, reading, etc.)

Last night I went to bed at: _____ pm/am

Last night I fell asleep in: _____ minutes

Last night, I woke up: _____ times

During those times, I was awake for: _____ minutes

Last night, I got out of bed: _____ times

Things that disturbed my sleep: _____

_____

(List any physical, mental, emotional, or environmental factors that affected your sleep.)

I slept for a total of: _____ hours

I got out of bed this morning at: _____ am/pm

Upon waking, I felt: __refreshed __groggy __exhausted

Answer the following questions at night.

During the day, I fell asleep or napped: _____ times

During my naps, I slept for: _____ minutes

During the day, I felt: __refreshed __groggy __exhausted

My caffeine consumption: _____ amount _____ time of day

Medications or sleep aids I took: _____

Exercise Your Body To Strengthen Your Brain

THE BEST WORKOUT FOR YOUR BRAIN IS A WORKOUT FOR YOUR BODY

Physical activity used to be a natural part of daily life for our ancestors. They hunted animals for food, tended to their gardens, built their own homes, and walked wherever they had to go. In our thoroughly modern world, we drive to work, take the escalator or elevator, sit at a desk all day, drive home, and loaf around on the couch. We've almost completely eliminated movement from our day-to-day lives. This is bad news for our brains — not to mention our bellies, butts, and backs.

If you want to have a healthy brain and body, you've got to get off your butt and move! Physical activity is the single most important thing you can do to enhance brain function and keep your body looking young. Whether you are six years old or 96 years old, exercise acts like a fountain of youth.

Physical exercise acts like a natural wonder drug for the brain. It improves the heart's ability to pump blood throughout the body, which increases blood flow to the brain. That supplies more oxygen, glucose, and nutrients to the brain, which enhances overall brain function. The number of ways that physical exercise benefits the brain is truly remarkable. Here are just some of the things exercise can do for your brain and body.

- Exercise encourages the growth of new brain cells.
- Physical activity enhances cognitive ability at all ages.

- Exercise burns calories.
- Exercise enhances your mood.
- Regular exercise helps alleviate depression.
- Physical activity calms worries and anxiety.
- Exercise helps prevent, delay, and lessen the effects of dementia and Alzheimer's disease.
- Vigorous aerobic exercise eases symptoms of ADD.
- Physical fitness sparks better behavior in adolescents.
- People who exercise regularly sleep better.
- Exercise helps women cope with hormonal changes.
- Exercise reduces the risk of high blood pressure, stroke, heart disease, diabetes, osteoporosis, breast cancer, and colon cancer.

Why our kids need to exercise more at school. Due to budget cuts and an increasing emphasis on test scores, many schools are cutting or eliminating physical education from the curriculum. This is terrible for our children! It is contributing to the problems of overweight and obesity and putting our children at risk for disease.

There are numerous scientific studies that show a strong relationship between physical fitness and academic achievement. Here is an example. In Dr. John J. Ratey's book, *Spark*, he details how a revolutionary physical education program at a school in Naperville, Illinois, has transformed the student body into some of the smartest kids in the nation. In 1999, eighth graders there took an international standards test that focuses on math and science. For years, U.S. students have been lagging far behind pupils from other nations in these two subjects. The Naperville eighth graders defied that trend, ranking first in the world in science and sixth in math. Compare those results to U.S. students' national rankings of eighteenth in science and nineteenth in math.

What's so special about Naperville's PE program? It sidelines traditional sports in favor of high-intensity aerobic activity — a brief warm-up, a one-mile run, and a cool-down. The only rule: students must keep their average heart rate above 185 for the mile-long run. The burst of activity is obviously paying off. I hope other schools from around the country take notice and start implementing similar PE programs. I highly recommend that you pick up a copy of *Spark* to learn more about the many ways this fitness program is benefiting the students.

Encouraging kids to engage in physical activity sets them up for a lifetime of better health. Evidence shows that kids who grow up exercising regularly are more likely to continue exercising as adults.

You can exercise anytime anywhere. If you think exercise can only be done in a gym with barbells or in an aerobics class, think again. There are many ways to squeeze physical activity into your daily life, whether you are at work, at home, or at school. Here are a few simple tricks to pack more exercise into your day.

- Take the stairs instead of the escalator or elevator.
- Walk to work or school.
- During work breaks, go for a brisk walk or do jumping jacks, push-ups, or knee lifts.
- Walk the kids to school instead of driving.
- Encourage young students to engage in physical activity.
- Take turns walking the dog.
- Do the housework at a quick pace.
- Walk to the grocery store instead of driving.
- Rake leaves, pull weeds, and mow the lawn.
- Stand up while you talk on the phone (the simple act of standing has been shown to burn more calories than sitting).

Which exercises are the best for the brain? Aerobic exercise plays a role in neurogenesis, the growth of new brain cells. Resistance training has been shown to have protective powers for the brain. Coordination activities activate the cerebellum, which enhances thinking, cognitive flexibility, and processing speed. Activities that combine aerobic exercise, resistance training, and coordination are fantastic for enhancing brain function.

My favorite physical activity is table tennis (also known as ping-pong), which also happens to be the world's best brain sport. It is highly aerobic and gets both the upper and lower body moving in every which way — twisting, bending down low, reaching up high, and shuffling from side to side. Plus, it gives your brain one heckuva workout.

Physical Activities for Your Brain Type

IF YOU HAVE:	TRY THIS TYPE OF EXERCISE:
PFC problems *ADD, short attention span,* *impulsiveness, poor planning*	LOTS of high-intensity aerobic activities, meditation
Basal ganglia problems *anxiety, panic attacks,* *constant worry*	Yoga, aerobic activity
Deep limbic problems *depression, PMS*	Aerobic activity in social activities like dancing
ACG problems *holding grudges, getting* *stuck on negative thoughts*	Intense aerobic exercise to boost serotonin
Temporal lobe problems *memory troubles*	Dancing or aerobics classes that involve music and steps
Cerebellum problems *slow thinking*	Coordination exercises

Brain Friendly Activities

Place a checkmark by the activities you enjoy or would like to try.

- ☐ Table tennis
- ☐ Tennis
- ☐ Dancing and/or dance classes
- ☐ Dance Dance Revolution (this is one video game that earns my seal of approval)
- ☐ Running
- ☐ Walking
- ☐ Golf (walk the course quickly, no carts please!)
- ☐ Hiking
- ☐ Frisbee
- ☐ Swimming
- ☐ Basketball
- ☐ Volleyball
- ☐ Jump rope
- ☐ Aerobics classes
- ☐ Badminton
- ☐ Martial arts (no contact and please don't break boards with your forehead!)
- ☐ Yoga (this isn't usually aerobic, but it's a great stress reliever!)
- ☐ Weight training – a pound of muscle burns 50 calories a day, while a pound of fat burns two calories a day. More muscle, less fat. I do light weight training most days that I work out to keep my muscles toned.

Here is your exercise homework: At the minimum, 30 minutes of intense exercise (which means to get your heart rate elevated) four to five times a week. Before embarking on this or any other exercise program, check with your physician to make sure you are healthy enough for regular exercise.

Work Your Brain

NEW LEARNING IS ESSENTIAL TO BOOSTING THE BRAIN'S POTENTIAL

I recently spoke at a conference for high-wealth individuals and I noticed that these millionaires shared a particular characteristic — they don't do repetitive things. They are always learning something new and challenging themselves to take on new ventures. New learning is one of the keys to brain health and, as the millionaires at this seminar show, wealth.

When it comes to the brain, you've got to use it or lose it. The same way you work out the muscles in your body, you need to exercise your brain for peak performance. In fact, the more you use your brain, the more you can use it. That's because new learning causes new connections to form in the brain. This type of mental stimulation is the best way to pump up your brain power throughout your entire life, and it is critical for everyone regardless of age.

Now for the "lose it" side of the equation: no learning has the opposite effect of new learning, causing the brain to start disconnecting itself. When this occurs, brain function suffers, and you or your loved ones begin to lose that mental edge. This can negatively affect your career, relationships, and health. It can also make you more vulnerable to memory problems in old age.

Most of us tend to find the things we're good at in life and then stick with them. And the things we aren't so good at? We typically avoid them like the plague. Got two left feet? You probably wouldn't be caught dead on the dance floor at weddings or parties. Have less-than-stellar hand-eye coordination? You almost certainly find excuses to avoid the company softball game. Have trouble solving crossword puzzles? You most likely toss that page of the newspaper straight into the trash. Unfortunately, this tendency isn't doing your brain any favors.

The best way to stay mentally fit is to try the things that don't come naturally to you. If you aren't a dancer, give square dancing or ballroom dancing a whirl. It will fire up areas of your brain you've been neglecting. With practice, you can actually improve your ability to boogie. You may not master the moves as well as the pros on *Dancing With the Stars*, but you might feel confident enough to strut your stuff at the next family wedding.

Rid yourself of the notion that you're good at some things because you inherited an innate ability, and you can't do others because you didn't get the right genes. It's what you do on a day-to-day basis that shapes your brain and regulates your skills.

Play brain healthy games. Whenever I tell people to play brain healthy games for mental exercise, they immediately assume that I'm talking about crossword puzzles or word games like Scrabble or Boggle. There's no doubt that these are great forms of mental exercise that shore up the language centers of the brain, but there are many other areas of the brain that need exercise too. The areas that control memory, concentration, attention, visual-spatial acuity, understanding, planning, anticipation, reaction, and coordination can also be strengthened with games. I recommend playing a variety of games and activities that work all the different parts of the brain to stay mentally fit.

Play creative games that activate the right side of the brain. For most of us, the left side of the brain, which is linked to things like logic and detail, is dominant. Because of this, it's a good idea to stimulate the more creative and artistic right side of the brain. Doing arts and crafts, playing with dolls or puppets, and playing charades help you access the right hemisphere.

Play board games that improve math skills. Another familiar board game, Monopoly, strengthens math skills and also requires strategizing and planning.

Play games and activities that involve coordination. If you want to have some fun while fueling brain cell growth, try juggling. One study showed that learning to juggle enhances the areas of your brain that control memory, language, and reading. Another study found that learning to juggle causes positive changes in the white matter of the brain, the bundles of nerve fibers that connect different parts of the brain.

Play games that involve music. Music and rhythm are housed in your temporal lobes, which also control memory, reading, and language.

Play strategy games that give multiple areas of the brain a workout. Chess is a time-honored strategy game that activates more parts of your brain than you might imagine.

Play memory games. Simple games, such as concentration, that can be played by anyone at any age help strengthen memory.

Play games that rely on visual power. Jigsaw puzzles offer a healthy dose of mental aerobics for all ages.

10 Ways to Exercise Your Brain

1. Spend at least 15 minutes a day — everyday — learning something new.

2. Take classes about something new and interesting at a local Learning Annex or community college.

3. Visit new places. Vacations and day trips are great for brains of any age.

4. Join a reading group. It can help protect your short-term memory.

5. Cross-train at work. Learn how to do a coworker's job or take on new tasks and responsibilities rather than doing the same thing over and over.

6. In college, sign up for courses and electives that aren't specifically related to your major.

7. Learn to play a musical instrument. Learning to tinkle the ivories or strum a guitar at any age enhances numerous brain functions, teaches the brain new patterns, and stimulates a variety of areas within the brain.

8. Strive to improve at your favorite activities. Challenge yourself to expand your skill set or enhance your knowledge.

9. Surround yourself with smart people. Spending time with people who challenge you intellectually can push your brain to new heights.

10. Shake up your routine. Following the same routine day after day dulls your brain. Shaking up the "same-old same-old" can stimulate new parts of your brain, make new connections, and increase your mental fitness.

10 Ways to Work My Brain

Write a list of things that are new and different for you.

1. _____

2. _____

3. _____

4. _____

5. _____

6. _____

7. _____

8. _____

9. _____

10. _____

My Daily Mental Workout

Every day, choose one or more things from your list that you will learn or practice today.

Sunday: _____

Monday: _____

Tuesday: _____

Wednesday:_____

Thursday: _____

Friday: _____

Saturday: _____

STEP 8

RELAX YOUR BRAIN

CALM THE STRESS THAT HARMS
YOUR BODY

These days, it seems like everybody is stressed out. The economy, relationship troubles, busy schedules, health issues, mental health problems, and demands at work, school, and home can affect your stress levels. Don't get me wrong. A little stress can be a good thing. When stress hits, the brain tells your body to start pumping out adrenaline (epinephrine) and cortisol, two hormones released by the adrenal glands (located above the kidneys). Within seconds, your heart starts to pound faster, your breathing quickens, your blood courses faster through your veins, and your mind feels like it's on heightened alert. You're ready for anything — running away from a would-be mugger, giving a speech in front of a roomful of peers, or taking the SAT exam.

These stress hormones are the primary chemicals of the "fight-or-flight" response and are especially useful when you face an immediate threat, such as a rattlesnake in your front yard (which happened to me once). Brief surges of stress hormones are normal and beneficial. They motivate you to do a good job at work, study before a test, or pay your bills on time. The problem with stress in our modern world is not these short bursts of adrenaline and cortisol. The problem is that for many of us, the stress reactions never stop — traffic, bills, work, school, family conflict, not enough sleep, health issues, and jam-packed schedules keep us in a constant state of stress.

How chronic stress harms your life. When stress gets out of control, it hurts the brain and can rip your life apart. Too much stress can actually kill you. Chronic stress has also been implicated in the following:

- Anxiety
- Depression
- Obesity
- Alzheimer's disease
- Heart disease
- Hypertension
- Cancer
- Disruption of sleep patterns
- Lowered immune system
- Reduced blood flow
- Premature aging
- Decreased brain reserve

When stress levels rise, we typically resort to all sorts of unhealthy ways to cope. We reach for the double cappuccino to help us power through the day. Due to the elevated levels of cortisol in our system, we tend to eat more, and we're more likely to give in to sugar and fat cravings. We skip our daily workouts because we're too busy. We skimp on sleep because we're too wired to doze off at night. We worry about how stressed out we are, which creates even more stress. Caffeine, poor eating habits, lack of exercise, and inadequate sleep decrease brain function and lower your ability to deal with stress. They are not good stress-management techniques!

Seven Brain Healthy Ways to Calm Stress

1. Meditate or pray on a regular basis. Decades of research have shown that meditation and prayer calm stress and enhance brain function. At the Amen Clinics, we performed a SPECT study on meditation and found that it significantly increases activity in the prefrontal cortex, which shows that mediation helps to tune people in, not out.

2. Learn to delegate and to say no. You don't have to accept every invitation, project, or opportunity that comes your way. When someone asks you to do something, a good first response would be, "Let me think about it." Then you can take the time to process the request to see if it fits with your schedule, desires, and goals.

3. Surround yourself with the sweet smell of lavender. This popular aroma has been the subject of countless research studies showing that it reduces cortisol levels and promotes relaxation and stress reduction.

4. Create a mental journal filled with positive memories. Through SPECT imaging, we have found that when people think about happy memories from the past, it enhances brain function.

5. Consider taking stress-busting supplements, such as *Dr. Daniel Amen's Nutraceutical Solutions: GABA Calming Support*, which contains supplements that have been found to promote relaxation and provide stress relief.

6. Practice diaphragmatic breathing. The simple act of breathing eliminates waste products, such as carbon dioxide, from the body. When there is too much carbon dioxide in your system, it can cause stressful feelings of disorientation and panic. Diaphragmatic breathing calms the basal ganglia, the area of the brain that controls anxiety, helps your brain run more efficiently, relaxes your muscles, warms your hands, and regulates your heartbeat. Here's how you do it. As you inhale,

let your belly expand. When you exhale, pull your belly in to push the air out of your lungs.

7. Practice gratitude. If you want your brain to work better, be grateful for the good things in your life. Focusing on the positive things in your life can make you happier regardless of your circumstances. At the Amen Clinics, we performed a SPECT study, which found that practicing gratitude causes real changes in your brain that enhance brain function and make you feel better.

STRESS-RELIEVING GRATITUDE EXERCISE #1: I'M GRATEFUL FOR...

Use the space provided, make copies of it, or just use a notepad to write down the things you are grateful for. The act of writing helps to solidify them in your brain. In my experience, when depressed patients did this exercise every day, they actually needed less antidepressant medication.

Five Things I'm Grateful For Today
Write out the things you are grateful for every day.

1. _____

2. _____

3. _____

4. _____

5. _____

STRESS-RELIEVING GRATITUDE EXERCISE #2: THE GLAD GAME

No matter what situation you are in, try to find something to be glad about. Think of a time when you were in a difficult or disappointing situation and started to think negatively but then found (or now can see) a "silver lining." Now, try to explain the same situation from a "glad" standpoint. What did you find to be glad about the situation?

_____

_____

_____

_____

_____

_____

STEP 9

Basic Training For Your Thinking

————————

DIRECT AND CORRECT YOUR BRAIN'S THOUGHTS

Do any of the following thoughts sound familiar?

"It is my wife's fault I'm fat, she puts too much food on my plate."

"Dieting is useless. I'm just going to gain the weight back."

"I don't need a lot of sleep — I'll just drink more coffee to stay awake."

"My memory is terrible, but that's normal since I'm over 45."

"There is nothing I can do to prevent wrinkles."

"I have no control over my high blood pressure — medicine is the only option."

If so, then you have been lying to yourself. These kinds of thoughts are lies, and they prevent you from getting the body and brain you want. You don't have to believe every lie that goes through your head. Even better, you can talk back to the lies.

Most of us never give thinking a second thought (pun intended). Thinking comes naturally to all of us. In all our years of education, nobody ever teaches us how to think, what to think, or what not to think. For many of us, it is a free-for-all in our minds, with random thoughts racing through without any rhyme or reason. For others of us, we get stuck on the same repetitive negative thoughts and can't get rid of them. Is this good for our brains? No! Is this good for our bodies? No! Our negative thinking has taken control of our brains, and we need to take control back. It is time for boot camp for your thinking. Improved brain function, a better figure, enhanced moods, greater immunity, and glowing skin will be your reward. All that just from thinking about thinking!

Your thoughts are powerful and they cause physical reactions in your brain and body. Bad, mad, sad, hopeless, or helpless thoughts release chemicals that make you feel bad. Your hands get cold, you start to sweat more, your heart rate quickens and flattens (which isn't good for your health), you breathe faster and more shallowly, and your muscles tense up. An Amen Clinics study showed that negative thinking causes serious decreases in activity in the cerebellum and temporal lobes. When activity in the cerebellum is low, it makes it harder for you to think and process information quickly — definitely not something you want to happen when you have to decide whether or not to supersize your meal at the fast-food restaurant.

On the other hand, happy, positive, hopeful, loving thoughts release chemicals that make you feel good. Your hands feel warmer, you sweat less, your heart rate slows and starts to bounce around (which is a good thing), your breathing slows and deepens, and your muscles relax. The same Amen Clinics study showed that positive thoughts enhance brain function.

Get rid of the ANTs (automatic negative thoughts) that infest your brain. ANTs are the negative thoughts that enter your head throughout the day, make you feel bad, and prevent you from adopting healthy behaviors. They sabotage your healthy eating plans, diminish your desire to exercise, destroy your self-esteem, and make you feel rotten. I came up with the concept of ANTs as a way to help my younger patients understand the notion of negative thoughts. One day, I came home to an ant invasion in my kitchen. I grabbed the bug spray and as I was spraying them, I thought,

"These ants are just like the thoughts inside my patients' brains." A few ants aren't a big deal, but when you have an infestation, it spoils your day. The ANTs in your head are just the same. A negative thought here and there isn't too troublesome, but if you have thousands of awful thoughts, it makes you feel awful.

Nine Species of ANTs

In my practice, I have identified nine "species" of ANTs that can steal your happiness and ruin your life.

1. **All or nothing:** Thinking that things are either all good or all bad. If you stick to an exercise plan for a month, you think you are the best athlete ever. If you miss a day at the gym, you give up your gym membership and go back to being a couch potato.

2. **Always thinking:** Overgeneralizing a situation and usually starting thoughts with words like *always, never, everyone, every time.*

3. **Focusing on the negative:** Preoccupying yourself with what's going wrong in a situation and ignoring the positive.

4. **Thinking with your feelings:** Believing your negative feelings without ever questioning them.

5. **Guilt beating:** Thinking with words like *should, must, ought,* or *have to* that produce feelings of guilt.

6. **Labeling:** Attaching a negative label to yourself or others.

7. **Fortune telling:** Predicting the worst.

8. **Mind reading:** Thinking you know what somebody else is thinking even though they have not told you and you have not asked them.

9. **Blame:** Blaming others for your problems.

Change your thinking, change your brain and body.
When you learn to challenge and correct negative, lying thoughts, you take away their power to control you and your body. Instead, by taking control of your thinking, you also take control of your actions and behaviors so you can enhance brain function and have a body you love. By changing your thinking, you can make yourself healthier, happier, and more successful. Here is a concept I use with a lot of my patients to help them take charge of their thinking.

Develop an ANTeater in your brain that can eat up all the negative thoughts that come into your head and mess up your life. Teach your ANTeater to talk back to the pesky ANTs so you can free yourself from negative thoughts. Whenever you feel mad, sad, nervous, or frustrated, write out your thoughts and the ANT species, then write down what your ANTeater would say to that ANT to kill it. As soon as you write down the truth, it diffuses any negative feelings, and you start to feel better. Look at the chart for examples of how to talk back to your ANTs.

Sample ANTeater Chart

ANT	Species	ANTeater
I ate a cookie. Now my diet is ruined.	All or nothing	I enjoyed the cookie and will eat fewer calories at dinner to make up for it.
I know I'm going to get Alzheimer's disease.	Fortune telling	I don't know that. If I take care of my brain now, I may not get it.
It is your fault.	Blame	I need to take responsibility for my actions and behaviors.

My ANTeater Chart
Whenever you feel mad, sad, nervous, or frustrated,
use the following chart to write out your thoughts and talk back
to them.

ANT	Species	ANTeater
_____ ____	_____	_____
_____ ____	_____	_____
_____ ____	_____	_____
_____ ____	_____	_____

Learn to direct your thinking to improve your life.
Clear, focused, written goals are essential to achieving what you want in life. They also strengthen your PFC, which is involved in planning and forethought. Your PFC needs clear direction. I have my patients do an exercise called the One-Page Miracle (OPM). It is extremely powerful. I call this exercise the One-Page Miracle because it makes such a dramatic difference in the lives of those who practice it.

Here are the steps: On a piece of paper, write down the specific goals you have for your life, including your health, relationships, work, and money. Then place it somewhere you are sure to see it everyday, such as on the refrigerator, on your bathroom mirror, or on your desk at work. This way, on a daily basis, you will be focusing on what's important to you. When you are focused on what you want, it makes it much easier to match your behavior to make it happen. Ask yourself everyday, "Is my behavior today getting me what I want?"

Sample One-Page Miracle
TAMARA'S ONE-PAGE MIRACLE
What Do I Want For My Life?

HEALTH — To best the healthiest person I can be

Weight: To lose 30 pounds so my body mass index (BMI) will be in the normal range.

Fitness: To exercise for at least 30 minutes four days a week.

Nutrition: To eat breakfast everyday so I don't get so hungry before lunchtime. To prepare a sack lunch at least three days a week so I'm not tempted to go to the fast-food restaurant across from work. To eliminate diet sodas and reduce the amount of sugar I eat. To take a multivitamin and fish oil supplement every day.

Physical Health: To lower my blood pressure and cholesterol levels.

Emotional Health: To meditate for 10 minutes every day to reduce stress.

RELATIONSHIPS — To be connected to those I love

Significant Other: To maintain a close, kind, caring, loving partnership with my husband. I want him to know how much I care about him.

Family: To be a firm, kind, positive, predictable presence in my children's lives. I want to help them develop into happy, responsible people. To continue to keep close contact with my parents, to provide support and love.

Friends: To take time to maintain and nurture my relationships with my siblings.

WORK — To be my best at work, while maintaining a balanced life. My work activities focus on taking care of my current projects, doing activities targeted at obtaining new clients, and giving back to the community by doing charity work each month. I will focus on my goals at work and not get distracted by things not directly related to my goals.

FINANCES — To be responsible and to help our resources grow

Short-term: To be thoughtful of how our money is spent, to ensure it is directly related to our family's and my needs and goals.

Long-term: To save 10 percent of everything I earn. I pay myself and my family before other things. I'll put this money away each month in a pension plan for retirement.

MY ONE-PAGE MIRACLE
What Do I Want For My Life?

HEALTH

Weight: _____
_____

Fitness: _____
_____

Nutrition: _____
_____

Emotional _____
Health: _____

RELATIONSHIPS

Significant _____
Other: _____

Family: _____
_____

Friends: _____
_____

WORK _____
_____

MONEY

Short-term: _____
_____

Long-term: _____
_____

Motivate Your Brain

IGNITE YOUR BRAIN CIRCUITS TO GET YOUR BRAIN IN GEAR

Behind every prosperous CEO, every thriving relationship, every excellent student, and every successful dieter, you will find a common element: motivation. Motivation is the hallmark of success. It sparks the chemical factories deep in the brain, lighting the emotional fires that drive us to love, care, want, need, crave, have to have, suffer, and create.

Motivation is the force behind the momentum of our lives. It provides the stimulus for becoming an entrepreneur or an admired gardener. It causes us to work 100 hours a week building a business or keeps us studying into our 30s to become a trauma surgeon. Motivation is what inspires you to travel hundreds or even thousands of miles to be in the arms of a new love or to change your diet to shed fat and improve your health.

Without motivation, little of consequence happens. You become stuck in boredom and mediocrity. Misdirected motivation can be even more harmful — it can get out of control and ruin lives. The key to success in every area of your life is directed motivation.

Learn the secret to directed motivation. When I do hypnosis for health and weight loss, I have people imagine themselves coming to a fork in the road. Down one road, they are continuing on a path of destruction and see what lays ahead if they continue to gain weight, leave their cholesterol and blood pressure out of control, and do not exercise. They can see that their bodies will continue to deteriorate. I want them to dwell on it to see if that is what they really want.

But if they take the other road — the road to a commitment to brain and body health, good food, exercise, new learning, stress reduction, and overall brain enhancement — they see their energy improving, their memory improving, their bodies trimming, and their important health numbers improving.

In order for you to consistently make the right decisions, you must have a burning desire to be healthy. Why do you care?

For me, I have an amazing wife, four wonderful children, and a new grandson, Elias. My grandfather was one of the most important people in my whole life. I was named after him and he was my best friend growing up. I know how important grandparents can be. The day Elias was born I thought about my grandfather all day long. I want to be healthy to be able to love Elias like my grandfather loved me. When I really think about what's important to me, no amount of cheeseburgers, doughnuts, or double fudge chocolate chip brownies is worth the price of damaging my health and stealing the time I have with my family.

You have to focus on your motivation ... or food, cigarettes, alcohol, video games, or some other bad brain habit will control you.

In the context of a healthy brain, the secret to motivation is to do what you love. How do you find what you love? What are the steps to discovering what motivates you? Think about the following to zero in on what makes you tick:

- What do you want?
- What must you have?
- What will you travel the world to find?
- What has excited you and moved you forward in the past?
- What currently excites you and is likely to excite you in the future?

For each area of your life — relationships, work, finances, physical, health, emotional, intellectual, and spiritual — list at least three to five times, general or specific, where you were turned on, excited, or felt maximum fun in your past and present life. Also, write about what you think would give you those same feelings in the future. My list for relationships is on the following page.

Relationships

PAST:

1. Falling in love, kissing my first love for hours

2. Being part of a big family, family gatherings, playing together

3. Competing at tennis, table tennis, basketball, anything

4. Doing work that makes a difference and is significant

PRESENT:

1. Being in love, making love, being close, talking for hours

2. Being a parent, encouraging, teaching, protecting, helping

3. Being helpful to those I love

4. Being part of a big family, family gatherings, playing together

5. Doing work that makes a difference and is significant

FUTURE:

1. Being in love, physical and emotional closeness, and connections

2. Being a parent and grandparent, encouraging, teaching, protecting, helping

3. Being part of a big family, family gatherings, playing together

4. Having friends all over the globe, finding mutual support and caring

5. Doing work that makes a difference and is significant

My Motivators

Relationships · Work · Finances · Health
Physical · Emotional · Intellectual · Spiritual

PAST:

1. _____

2. _____

3. _____

4. _____

PRESENT:

1. _____

2. _____

3. _____

4. _____

FUTURE:

1. _____

2. _____

3. _____

4. _____

Get to know the motivational robbers and motivational enhancers. Motivational enhancers are active thoughts and steps you choose to take each second of your day toward the goal of optimum brain and body health. Motivational robbers are the thoughts and choices you make that rob you of brain health and well being.

Consider for a moment what has motivated you in the past. What helped you take risks and steps in the direction toward reaching your goals? Motivational enhancers can include:

- Favorite movies
- Favorite songs
- Favorite books
- Motivational tapes of successful people sharing their stories of how they rose above their circumstances to make extraordinary life changes.

Practice neuro-visual training. Neuro-visual conditioning exercises, like the one described here for weight loss, can help you achieve your goals.

1. Close your eyes, take a deep breath, and exhale.

2. Continue to breathe deeply. With each exhale, feel the tension and anxiety of each muscle in your body releasing and send every thought, feeling, situation, and person that causes pain into a container of your choosing. This container is strong enough to hold everything and anything that you want to place into that container.

3. Take a few minutes as you place each distressing thought, feeling, and motivational robber in your life into that container.

4. When you have put all your motivational robbers in it, seal it up with an imaginary valve that allows you to open it

without letting anything spill out but allows you to put more in.

5. Place a sign on it that says that you will deal with what is in there at the right time and in a healthy way.

6. Now that you are relaxed, picture yourself at your ideal weight — moving with the freedom and flexibility you have always wanted. See yourself wearing the clothes you want to wear, interacting with people in the way you want to interact with them.

7. Picture yourself taking steps toward the intellectual, emotional, physical, and financial goals that you want to reach.

8. When that image is compelling and you are feeling it in every cell of your body, say a trigger word or phrase that means something to you (for example: " I can do it…!").

9. As you say that word or phrase, press your thumb and forefinger together. Keep repeating your trigger word or phrase and touching your fingers together.

10. Each time you repeat it, enjoy the feeling of satisfaction, well-being, competence, and excitement at the thought of reaching your goal.

11. Each time you say the word or phrase and press your forefinger and thumb together, you are anchoring this neuro-visual-body experience deeper and deeper into your mind and body. Your brain and body begin working together for your well-being.

After you have done the above exercise, think of a stressful situation coming up that you are going to face and then trigger the neuro-visual-body response of the above experience by pressing your forefinger and thumb together. Rehearse this several times by yourself, and then train yourself to trigger that response as you are about to face stressful situation.

List the motivational enhancers that have helped you and then write an example of how that particular enhancer helped you.

Example: Youtube clip of Susan Boyle singing on the TV show *Britain's Got Talent*

After I watched Susan Boyle sing "I Dreamed A Dream," I decided to take a step toward my dream of going to graduate school by completing and mailing the application forms that I had been putting off.

_____

_____

_____

_____

_____

_____

Motivational robbers are the thoughts and actions that take the steam out of the momentum we are building to take the second-by-second steps necessary for brain and body health. Motivational robbers can also be situations or relationships that we allow to sabotage our steps toward health.

As an example, one of my patients described how he would allow his wife to rob his motivation to keep peace in his marriage and household. He had gotten up early one morning, made breakfast for the family, and picked up his gym bag to head for the health club. His wife looked at him and said, "You are not going to go work out and leave me with this mess of a kitchen to clean up while you spend the entire morning at the health club, are you?"

He dropped his bag, walked back into the kitchen and began to clean up. While he was cleaning up, he felt irritated at himself for choosing kitchen duty over the gym and also managed to finish off the leftovers from breakfast. By the time he finished, his desire to go to the health club was gone. He got busy with stuff around the house and yard for the rest of the day and did not get the exercise he had committed himself to do to reach his weight-loss goals.

List some motivational robbers in your life.

_____

_____

_____

_____

_____

_____

Now take each of those motivational robbers and write out a different response to the scenario.

_____

_____

_____

_____

_____

_____

Now spend time rehearsing that different response in that stressful experience. My patient wrote out the following response to the above situation:

"Thank you for reminding me. I did forget to clean up the kitchen and do the dishes. It will take me 15 minutes to finish that up, then I will be back from the health club in 1½ hours. How about I take care of the kids when I get back so you can have some time to yourself?"

Five Tips to Maintain High Motivation Towards Brain and Body Health

1. Be proactive: As you plan your day, write down in your journal what you are going to build into your day to enhance motivation.

2. Write out a list of five people you can call, share what you are going through, and allow them to encourage you.

3. Spend time each day visualizing or picturing the goals you want to reach. Develop a compelling visualization, and anchor that visualization in your mind and body.

4. Write out some motivational robbers that you will face each day and write out how you are going to think and act in those situations. Rehearse those situations in your mind prior to facing them.

5. Look for a seminar, talk, or program that will help inspire you and motivate you.

STEP 11

Overcoming The Barriers
To Living A Brain Healthy Life

_____

DEALING WITH FOOD PUSHERS, ENERGY
ZAPPERS, MONEY CONCERNS, AND MORE

Maria is one of my patients who has started doing a 30-minute fast walk every morning before work in an effort to lead a more brain healthy life. But several days a week, her husband Ben tries to coax her into staying in bed and going back to sleep.

Jason wants to reduce stress and improve his sleeping habits. He knows that regular exercise and supplements can alleviate stress and promote relaxation, but he's worried about the cost of a gym membership and supplements so he doesn't exercise or get the nutrients he needs.

I recently became a grandfather for the first time and couldn't wait to visit my new grandchild. When I went to my daughter's home, my sister was visiting her, too. She asked me if I wanted to eat, and I said no, I wasn't hungry. I thought that would be the end of that discussion, but she continued to ask me an additional five times if I wanted something to eat!

Food pushers, energy zappers, money concerns — these are all things that can stand in the way of your efforts to adopt a brain healthy life. When you start living a brain healthy life, it can make those around you uncomfortable, especially if they have a lot of bad brain habits. Deep down, some people — even those who love you the most —don't want you to succeed because it will make them feel like more of a failure. For others, their habits are so ingrained that they simply don't know how to react to your new lifestyle. Many of my patients notice this kind of behavior with their families, friends, and coworkers.

Food pushers can sabotage a brain healthy diet. As a society, we're bombarded with bad messages about food. TV commercials, billboards, and radio ads are constantly encouraging us to adopt bad eating habits. Restaurants and fast-food joints train employees to "upsell" as a way to increase sales and subsequently, expand our waistlines. Here are some of the sneaky tactics food sellers use to try to get you to eat and drink more.

- Do you want to supersize that for only 39 cents?
- Do you want fries with your meal?
- Do you want bread first? (This makes you hungrier so you eat more!)
- Do you want an appetizer?
- Do you want another drink?
- Do you want a larger drink? It is a better deal!

Your response to all of these questions should always be, "No!" Eating or drinking more than you need just because it's more economical will cost you far more in the long run. Unfortunately, spouses, friends, coworkers, neighbors, and even children can also make it very difficult for you to stay on track.

Food pushers are also evident in our nation's offices and even our schools. At work, you find a bowl of candy on the receptionist's desk, doughnuts in the break room, and pastries at meetings. Plus, there are the vending machines filled with high-fat, high-sugar, high-salt snacks.

Even more troubling are the food pushers in our schools. Government-subsidized school lunches include things like corn dogs, pizza pockets, tater tots, cupcakes, and chocolate milk with high fructose. This is what we are teaching our children to eat, and it is one of the reasons why so many kids are overweight or obese and at increased risk of developing type 2 diabetes in their lifetime.

School lunches aren't the only problem in schools. My wife, Tana, has been looking at private schools for our six-year-old daughter, Chloe, and recently visited one that has a great reputation. Tana couldn't believe it when she saw that they were teaching the kids to count using candy corn! This is not brain healthy!

Learning to deal with and say no to food pushers in the home, on the town, at work, and at school is critical to your success.

15 Tips For Dealing With Food Pushers

1. Ask your spouse and kids to hide unhealthy treats and snacks out of view so you don't have to be tempted by them.

2. If you are going to a dinner with friends or family, call ahead to inform the host that you are on a special brain healthy diet and won't be able to eat certain foods.

3. If you are at a business luncheon, and your new boss or a potential client raves about how wonderful the bread is and offers it to you, take one small bite, tell them it is delicious, and then wait for your meal.

4. When going to parties, consider eating at home first so you won't be hungry at the event.

5. Be upfront with food pushers. Explain that you are trying to eat a more balanced diet, and that when they offer you cake, chips, or pizza, it makes it more difficult for you.

6. Instead of going out to lunch or dinner with friends, choose activities that aren't centered around food, such as going for a walk.

7. If your coworkers invite you to happy hour, but you don't want them to push you to drink alcohol, ask the bartender to put

fizzy water or juice in a bar glass and garnish it with something that makes it look like an alcoholic drink.

8. When people offer seconds, tell them you are pleasantly full. If they insist, explain that you are trying to watch your calories. If they continue to push extra helpings on you, ask them why they are bent on sabotaging your efforts to be healthy.

9. I know some people who will accept a piece of cake or a cocktail and then toss it in the trash or the sink as soon as the host turns away.

10. Avoid visiting with coworkers who have a bowl of candy on their desk, and if possible, choose a route that doesn't go past the break room or the vending machines.

11. Tell your host you don't drink alcohol… period.

12. With hosts you don't know well and likely won't see again, consider telling them you have a medical problem, such as a food allergy.

13. Eat very slowly so when the host starts asking guests if they want seconds, you can say you are still working on your first helping. By the time you have finished, the second round of eating could be over, and you won't have to be subjected to the offer for more.

14. Give kids a healthy sack lunch so they don't have to eat from the cafeteria, if schools serve unhealthy food.

15. Commit yourself to taking control of your own body and don't let other people make you fat and stupid.

Energy zappers try to prevent you from getting the exercise you need. When an energy zapper tries to keep you from exercising, let them know why it's important to you and why it is also beneficial to them. Arm yourself with responses like these:

- "I'm exercising because it makes me feel good and helps keep me healthy by preventing serious conditions like high blood pressure and heart disease. If you care about me and my health, you won't ask me to skip it."

- "Physical activity puts me in a better mood, which will help our relationship and make me a better partner/friend."

The people around you aren't the only energy zappers. There are many other things that will rob you of energy, including:

- Inherited brain disorders
- Infectious causes
- Hormonal issues
- Anemia
- Brain trauma
- Environmental toxins
- Many medications
- Chronic stress
- Caffeine
- Smoking
- Poor eating habits
- Poor sleep
- Too much alcohol
- Lack of exercise
- Untreated past emotional trauma
- Low/erratic blood sugar states from any cause

Things that will boost your energy include:

- Treat the energy robbers described above.
- Get at least seven hours of sleep.
- Eat a brain healthy diet.
- Maintain a level blood sugar.
- Exercise four to five times a week.
- Use stress-reduction techniques.
- Test and optimize hormone levels.
- Meditate.
- Eat low-calorie, high-fiber foods (fruits, vegetables, beans, and whole grains).
- Drink green tea, which includes theanine.
- Take supplements, such as *Dr. Daniel Amen's Nutraceutical Solutions: Focus & Energy Optimizer.*

Money concerns affect many people. Fortunately, I can tell you that living a brain healthy life doesn't have to cost a lot of money. In fact, the majority of tips in this book are completely free. Here is a list of low-cost or free ways to improve brain health.

50 Free and Low-Cost Ways to Improve Brain Health

1. Loving your brain is free.

2. Talking about the brain with family, friends, coworkers, and classmates is free.

3. Looking for news items about the brain is free.

4. Keeping a daily journal is free.

5. Becoming aware of the various brain systems is free.

6. Understanding your own brain and how it affects your life is free.

7. Avoiding activities at high risk for brain injury is free.

8. Putting a halt to drug use saves money.

9. Limiting your exposure to toxins like nail polish and hair chemicals is free.

10. Cooking healthy food at home is less expensive than eating out.

11. Buying frozen fruits in bulk is an inexpensive way to get your antioxidants.

12. Buying frozen vegetables in bulk is another low-cost option.

13. Stocking up on brain healthy beans is an inexpensive way to get more fiber in your diet.

14. Skipping candy, cookies, and ice cream lowers your food bill.

15. Eating fewer calories costs less.

16. Eating five or six small meals doesn't cost any more than eating three big meals.

17. Saying no to supersizing your meal saves money.

18. At restaurants, splitting meals cuts the check in half.

19. Skipping the appetizers and desserts lowers your check.

20. Cutting out the alcohol can significantly reduce your bill.

21. Quitting smoking saves money spent on cigarettes.

22. Getting more sleep is free.

23. Drinking water costs less than drinking energy drinks, coffee, or sodas.

24. Exercising outdoors is free.

25. Thinking positive thoughts is free.

26. Cutting TV time is free.

27. Limiting videogame playing is free.

28. Buying fewer video games saves money.

29. Limiting Internet time is free.

30. Limiting texting can save money.

31. Cutting caffeine can cut your Starbucks bill.

32. Getting books from the library for new learning is free.

33. Getting foreign language CDs from the library is free.

34. Games and puzzles are a low-cost investment for mental workouts.

35. Classes at local community colleges and the Learning Annex are relatively inexpensive.

36. Improving at your favorite activities can be free.

37. Shaking up your daily routine is free.

38. Surrounding yourself with smart people is free.

39. Meditation is free.

40. Prayer is free.

41. Saying no to invitations is free.

42. Being grateful is free.

43. Deep breathing for stress reduction is free.

44. Self-hypnosis is free.

45. Soothing music doesn't require a big investment.

46. Focusing on positive memories is free.

47. Talking back to your ANTs is free.

48. Writing down your goals is free.

49. Staying focused on what motivates you is free.

50. Saying no to food pushers who want you to buy unhealthy fare can save money.

On the other hand, there are times when it is well worth it to spend money on your health and well-being. You may be able to use some of the money you save from the tips above to cover these costs.

- Getting a complete physical is important to check for medical conditions that might be affecting brain health.

- Taking a daily multivitamin and fish oil supplement to ward off disease and protect brain health.

- Seeing a professional for a brain disorder.

When seeking professional help for a brain disorder, remember that it is important to find the right person for your needs rather than seeking out the one who charges the least amount of money. The right professional can have a very positive impact on your career, your relationships, and your health. The wrong professional can make things worse in every area of your life. Saving money upfront can cost you in the long run. The right help is not only cost effective but also saves you unnecessary pain and suffering.

The same principle applies if you need help losing weight. Money spent on proven programs that can teach you how to reach your goals in a healthy way can pay off over time. Overweight and obesity are associated with many medical conditions that can be far more costly to you over time. In addition, one study showed that obese women in white-collar jobs earned about 30 percent less than thinner women in the same jobs. Losing weight can improve your confidence so you can pursue your career goals, become more successful, and earn more money.

My Obstacles to Brain Health	How I Will Deal With These Obstacles

STEP 12

Identify And Treat
Brain Problems Early

NORMAL IS A MYTH,
WE ALL NEED A LITTLE HELP

"The normal man is a fiction." — *Carl Jung*

"The only normal people are the ones you don't know too well."
— *Rodney Dangerfield*

J ack was typical of many of the people who come to my clinics.
Even though he was a competent, high level computer executive,
he struggled with his mood and temper. He was so ashamed of his
shortcomings that he avoided getting help until his wife threatened
to divorce him (a very common scenario in our clinics). When I
first saw him he said that he thought everyone else was normal
except him, everyone else was saner, better looking, more
confident, had more sex and in general had a better time in life
than he was having.

As I listened, my first thought was that he should spend a
week with me, which would completely dispel his notion that
everyone else was normal. Then I remembered a time early in my
psychiatric career when this odd thing kept happening to me. It
seemed that any time I got the idea that someone was really great,
normal, healthy, and had it all together, within three weeks he or
she would be in my office telling me about the pain, stress,
traumas, sins, or disappointments in his or her own life. It
happened so often that I started to believe that we all needed a little
help.

Here are two brief examples:

1. One of the physicians at Fort Irwin, an Army Post in the middle of the Mojave Desert where I spent two years as the chief of the community mental health center, had a barbeque at his house to welcome me when I first arrived at this isolated duty assignment. I met his wife and kids and had a wonderful time. I remember how much I admired him. Even though he was "very Army" for a military doctor, he was smart, competent and seemed to truly care about the soldiers we were serving. Three weeks later, his wife came to my office in tears and said how worried she was about his drinking. As it turned out, this physician had a serious drinking problem and was eventually sent to an inpatient program to get clean and sober.

2. One of my best friends through the years is a military chaplain. He is a kind, sensitive man with a big heart and a sharp wit. His soldiers loved him and he was rapidly promoted. I remember one particular day when I was thinking about how much I admired him, when I got an urgent message that he had called. When I phoned him back he was in a panic and had to see me right away. It was toward the end of the day so I met him at the Officer's Club for dinner.

   I listened to him tell me about another side of himself well into the evening. During the day he had lost four hours of time and was afraid he was losing his mind. He did not know how he got to work or where his car was parked. And this was not the first time it happened. It turned out that he had a multiple personality disorder from severe childhood abuse, which he never told me about until he felt as though he was cracking up. I was saddened by his suffering and amazed at how functional he was given the multitude of traumas in his life.

   A quick look at some of the statistics on mental illness will put to rest anyone's notions that the vast majority of people are without pain. According to the Epidemiological Catchment Study sponsored by the National Institutes of Mental Health, 51 percent of the United States population at some point in their lives will suffer from a psychiatric (brain) illness, with anxiety, depression, and substance abuse being the most common. Twenty-nine percent of the population will have two psychiatric illnesses and 17 percent will have three. Millions of people suffer, yet many think that others have it better. Most people have no idea how lucky they really are. It is normal to have struggles, and it is better to count your blessings rather than to feel messed up.

When I first started my brain-imaging work, I was not very concerned with the concept of normal, because I had so many sick people to try to help. Over the years, however, building a database of normal people has become essential to my work. In our database, we have over 75 murderers and hundreds of violent people. We needed normal people to do comparison studies. We also have thousands of patients with ADD, anxiety, depression, brain trauma, substance abuse, and bipolar disorder. A normal group became essential in studying our patient group and being able to understand and publish our results.

I knew that finding normal people would be a challenge. The people whom I thought were normal often ended up in my office asking for help. Still, I had no idea how hard it would be to find truly normal brains. For our research project, we had fairly strict criteria for normal. The strictness was essential to our work and being able to publish our studies.

To be in our study people had to meet five criteria:

- No psychiatric illness at any point in their lives (that eliminated 51 percent of the population)
- No significant head injuries
- No substance abuse
- No neurological problems
- No first-degree relative (mother, father, sibling, or child) with a psychiatric illness, including substance abuse problems.

In addition, participants were thoroughly interviewed about the above issues, given a structured psychiatric screening test, the Minnesota Multiphasic Personality Inventory (MMPI), which is a test of personality, and a memory screening test.

I recruited people from within my own family (not the best place to start, except for my mother who has a drop dead perfect brain), my parents' country club, churches, schools, by placing ads in the *Los Angeles Times*, placing flyers at local universities in student and teacher boxes, and even at my lectures. After five years, we had screened over 3,000 people and had only scanned 90 "normal" people. About one in 33 people who thought they were normal actually met our criteria. Here is an example.

Steve was a youth pastor who worked in a local church. He saw himself as kind, competent, and perfectly normal. His wife on the other hand, saw him as someone who was temperamental, rigid, and moody. A more detailed history from his mother revealed that he had a serious head injury as a child, where he fell backwards from the top of a swing onto his head and sustained a brief loss of consciousness.

The research team was amazed at how many people who thought of themselves as not only normal, but almost perfect, were in reality troubled with mood or attentional problems or they had histories of serious brain injuries or forgotten substance abuse. As part of the screening process, we had spouses and parents fill out information on study subjects to make sure we always had another person's point of view.

Halfway through, we changed the name of the study from the Amen Clinics Normal Study to the Amen Clinics Healthy Brain Study. Some might think that the name change was just a subtle difference. Not to us. We now believe that normal is a myth and truly healthy brains are actually rare. There are very few really healthy brains among us. We all need a little help. This idea is actually comforting to me. It lessens judgment because it is hard to say, "I am better than you." It helps us see that a brain health is fragile and needs to be taken seriously. And, as a society, we need to make brain health a priority.

Along the same lines, we have found that many people who struggle do not know that there are problems. Did you know that 95 percent of people who have Alzheimer's disease are not diagnosed until they are in the moderate to severe stages of the illness? Clearly, it is much better to know that a problem is brewing early so you can implement prevention and treatment strategies as soon as possible. Many people do not know that they have sustained brain injuries that have affected their lives. Many people also have no idea that they have mood or attentional problems, yet ask their spouses and you will get an ear full.

When I turned 40, I got a routine eye exam. To my surprise, I could not see past five feet out of my left eye. I was in serious need of glasses, yet I had no idea. If we all need a little help, then early screening is an essential tool to keeping our brains healthy as we age.

If you suffer with symptoms such as anxiety, panic, obsessions, compulsions, depression, mood swings, substance abuse, addictive behaviors, attentional problems, or impulsivity, getting a competent evaluation and treatment for these problems early will enhance your overall life and success. Left untreated, these problems can ruin your life. The questionnaire you took to start this program screened for ADD, anxiety, depression, obsessive issues, temporal lobe problems and memory issues.

One of the most important lessons I have learned from looking at tens of thousands of SPECT scans is that what most people think of as mental illnesses, such as anxiety, depression, bipolar disorder or ADD, are really in large part brain problems and getting the right help for these issues is essential to creating a brain healthy life.

For example, if you have attention deficit disorder or ADD, which is generally associated with low activity in the prefrontal cortex, you are more likely to have trouble controlling your behavior and you may say the first thought that comes into your head. In one study, 75 percent of people with untreated ADD had relationship problems. Why? Think of the people you know who are married. Is it helpful for them to say everything they think in their marriage? Of course not! Relationships require tact. They require forethought. But when you have low activity in the prefrontal cortex, you often say the first thing that comes into your mind, which can get you into big trouble.

If you struggle with any of these problems then I say welcome to normal. I tell my patients that "normal" is really nothing more than a setting on a dryer or a city in Illinois.

Actually, I once gave a lecture in Normal, IL. It was great fun. I got to go to the Normal grocery store. I was interviewed on the Normal radio station. And I was finally able to meet Normal women. As it turned out, people from Normal had the same problems that I had seen everywhere else.

Psychiatric illnesses are not single or simple disorders. From our brain-imaging work, I have learned that most psychiatric illnesses have multiple types and that giving someone the diagnosis of depression is exactly like giving them the diagnosis of chest pain.

In a previous Step, I discussed why doctors don't give people the diagnosis of chest pain — because it is a symptom with many different causes. The same thing is true for depression. It is a symptom with many different causes, and one treatment does not fit everyone. What can cause depression? So many different things, from chronic stress, relationship problems, head injuries, drug abuse, low thyroid levels, medications, genetic tendencies, and grief.

With our brain-imaging work we have seen that depression has at least seven different patterns. You can have too much activity in the front part of your brain and overthink or worry yourself sick, or you can have too little activity in this part of the brain and have trouble thinking or controlling your impulses. Depression is not just one thing and giving everyone the same treatment for it invites disaster. Yet, that is exactly what is happening across our country every day. Many patients tell their doctors that they are depressed and leave the office after a five-minute appointment with samples of the latest drug, without any sense of the type of depression they are treating.

Here is an example. Jan left her family doctor's office with a prescription for Prozac. She told him that she had been under a lot of stress and was feeling sad. Within a week she started to feel better. Within two weeks she was feeling fabulous. But after she had two brief affairs and spent $25,000 she didn't have, Jan's family figured out that she had bipolar disorder that was triggered by the new medicine.

Knowing the type of depression, ADD, or anxiety you have is critical to getting the right help. In our clinics, we use brain SPECT imaging to help us understand and treat the brains of our patients. But a long time ago, I realized that not everyone is able to get a scan. My books are translated into 26 languages and if you read one in China or Brazil, odds are you are not going to get a scan any time soon.

So based on thousands of scans, I developed a series of questionnaires, including the one highlighted in this program, to help people predict what their scan *might* look like if they could get one. Then, based on the answers, as you have seen, I give suggestions on ways to think about helping the brain with certain natural supplements, medications, or exercises. The questionnaires are used by mental health professionals around the world. Of course, you should always talk with your doctor about your own individual situation.

Even after doing all of the brain healthy strategies in this book, some people will still need to seek professional help. Some people will need psychotherapy. Some will need more directed guidance with supplements or other alternative treatments. Some will need medication. In lecturing around the world, I am frequently asked the following questions:

- When is it time to see a professional about my brain?
- How do I go about finding a competent professional?

When is it time to see a professional about my brain? This question is relatively easy to answer. People should seek professional help when their behaviors, feelings, thoughts, or memory (all brain functions) interfere with their ability to reach their potential in their relationships, work, academics, or health.

How do I go about finding a competent professional? At the Amen Clinics, we receive many calls and emails from around the world looking for competent professionals who think in similar ways to the principles outlined in this book. We maintain a list of colleagues on our website at www.amenclinics.com. Because our approach to optimizing brain health is new, other professionals who know and practice this information may be hard to find. However, finding the right professional for evaluation and treatment is critical to the healing process.

There are a number of steps to take in finding the best person to assist you. Search for the best. If he or she is on your insurance plan — great, but don't let that be the primary criteria. Once you get the names of competent professionals, check their credentials. Very few patients ever check a professional's background. Board certification is a positive credential.

Set up an interview with the professional to see whether or not you want to work with him or her. Generally, you have to pay for their time, but it is worth spending the money to get to know the people you will rely on for help.

Also, look for a person who is open-minded, up-to-date, and willing to try new things. Look for a person who treats you with respect, listens to your questions, and responds to your needs. Look for a relationship that is collaborative and respectful.

Make sure to get your brain tuned up and any brain problems treated in order to be your best self, both physically and emotionally.

APPENDIX A

Important Numbers To Know

Here are some important numbers you need to know to maintain a healthy brain and body. Some of these have been discussed throughout the book, and some are new.

1. **Body Mass Index (BMI)**:
   BMI = weight (lb) x 703 / height^2 (inches^2)

2. **Daily caloric needs to maintain current body weight**: To find out your basic calorie needs without exercise, which is referred to as your resting basal metabolic rate (BMR), fill out the following equation:

   - Women: 655 + (4.35 x current weight in pounds) + (4.7 x height in inches) - (4.7 x age in years)

   - Men: 66 + (6.23 x current weight in pounds) + (12.7 x height in inches) – (6.8 x age in years)

   Take that number and multiply by it by the appropriate number below.

   - 1.2 — if you are sedentary (little or no exercise)
   - 1.375 — if you are lightly active (light exercise/sports 1-3 days/week)
   - 1.55 — if you are moderately active (moderate exercise/sports 3-5 days/week)
   - 1.75 — if you are very active (hard exercise/sports 6-7 days a week)
   - 1.9 — if you are extra active (very hard exercise/sports and a physical job or strength training twice a day)

To find out how many calories you need to eat to reach your goal weight, simply substitute your goal weight for your current weight in the equation above.

3. **Average daily calories you consume** (don't lie to yourself): It is very helpful for you to keep a log of everything you put into your mouth.

4. **Desired weight:** Set a realistic goal for your weight and match your behavior to reach it.

5. **Number of hours you sleep at night:** Don't fool yourself into thinking you only need a few hours of sleep. Here are the average sleep requirements by age according to the National Sleep Foundation and the National Institute of Neurological Disorders and Stroke.

Age Range	Number of Hours of Sleep
1-3 years old	12-14 hours
3-5 years old	11-13 hours
5-12 years old	10-11 hours
13-19 years old	9 hours
Adults	7-8 hours
Seniors	7-8 hours

6. **Vitamin D level:** Have your physician check your 25-hydroxy vitamin D level, and if it is low take a vitamin D supplement.

Low < 30
Optimal between 50-90
High > 90

7. **Thyroid level:** Have your doctor check your free T3 and TSH levels to check for hypothyroidism or hyperthyroidism and treat as necessary to normalize.

8. **C-reactive protein**: This is a measure of inflammation that your doctor can check with a simple blood test. Elevated

inflammation is associated with a number of diseases and conditions and should prompt you to eliminate bad brain habits.

9. **Homocysteine level**: This is another marker of inflammation.

10. **HgA1C**: This test shows your average blood sugar levels over the past two to three months and is used to diagnose diabetes and prediabetes. According to Lab Tests Online, normal results for a nondiabetic person are in the range of 4 to 6 percent. Numbers higher than that may indicate diabetes.

11. **Fasting blood sugar**: This test usually requires that you fast for about eight hours prior to having your blood drawn. It evaluates your blood sugar levels solely for the day when you have your blood drawn. Here is what the levels mean according to the American Diabetes Association:

    Normal — 70-99 mg/dL
    Prediabetes — 100-125 mg/dL
    Diabetes — 126 mg/dL or higher

12. **Cholesterol**: Make sure your doctor checks your total cholesterol level as well as your HDL (good cholesterol), LDL (bad cholesterol), and triglycerides (a form of fat). According to the American Heart Association, optimal levels are as follows:

    Total cholesterol — less than 200
    HDL — 60 or higher
    LDL — less than 100
    Triglycerides — less than 150

13. **Blood pressure:** Have your doctor check your blood pressure at your annual physical or more often if it is high. Here is how to interpret the numbers, according to the American Heart Association:

    Below 120 over 80 — optimal

120-139 over 80-89 — prehypertension
140   or above) over 90 (or above) — hypertension

14. **Know how many of the 12 most common preventable causes of death you have, then decrease them.**

1. Smoking
2. High blood pressure
3. BMI indicating overweight or obese
4. Physical inactivity
5. High fasting blood glucose
6. High LDL cholesterol
7. Alcohol abuse
8. Low levels of omega-3 fatty acids
9. High dietary saturated fat intake
10. Low polyunsaturated fat intake
11. High dietary salt
12. Low intake of fruits and vegetables

APPENDIX B

100 Ways To Leave
Your Blubber

BREAKFAST

1. If you want a bagel, choose a store-bought one that comes with a food label so you know how many calories it has rather than one from the bakery that may have double the calories.

2. Use all-fruit, no-sugar-added jams for bagels or toast. This helps to get rid of the extra sugar and calories. Smuckers makes a 100 percent spreadable fruit line.

3. Replace bacon at breakfast with reduced-fat turkey bacon or Canadian bacon.

4. Indulge in modified French toast. Use nonfat milk and egg whites instead of whole milk and eggs.

5. Eat breakfast every day. People who skip breakfast are four times more likely to be fatter than people who don't skip breakfast! Research suggests that those who lose weight are better at keeping it off if they have breakfast in the morning.

6. Don't reach for the bacon, eggs, and pancake special (lots of bad things found here), rather a 200- to 300-calorie protein-blueberry shake is a good brain-healthy way to start the day.

7. Top your cereal with low-fat or fat-free milk instead of 2 percent or whole milk.

8. Use a nonstick pan and cooking spray (rather than butter) to scramble or fry eggs.

9. Try my favorite butter substitute: Earth Balance Natural Buttery Spread With Olive Oil. It has no trans fats and cuts about 20 calories per serving compared to real butter or margarine.

10. Eat only the egg white and toss away the yolk to trim about 60 calories.

LUNCH

11. Replace 1 tablespoon of regular mayo on your turkey sandwich with 1½ tablespoons of reduced-fat mayo.

12. Add more vegetables, such as cucumbers, lettuce, tomato, and onions to a sandwich instead of extra meat or cheese.

13. Accompany a sandwich with salad or fruit instead of chips or French fries.

14. Choose vegetable-based broth soups rather than cream- or meat-based soups.

15. Stop putting butter, margarine, or mayonnaise on your sandwiches. Use mustard instead.

16. Use water-packed tuna instead of tuna packed in oil.

17. Skip the slice of cheese on your sandwich to save about 100 calories.

DINNER

18. Steam veggies instead of sautéing them in butter or oil.

19. Switch to boiled shrimp instead of steak on shish kebabs.

20. Broil or bake foods instead of frying them.

21. Try lemon juice to flavor vegetables.

22. When having pizza, choose vegetables as toppings and just a light sprinkling of cheese instead of fatty meats.

23. Modify recipes to reduce the amount of fat and calories. For example, when making lasagna, use part-skim ricotta cheese instead of whole-milk ricotta cheese. Substitute shredded vegetables, such as carrots, zucchini, and spinach for some of the ground meat in lasagna.

24. Eat sweet potatoes, which contain cellulose and hemicelluloses, insoluble fibers that help you feel full faster so you eat less.

25. Use fresh herbs and garlic whenever possible to add a lot of flavor with little to no calories.

26. Brown and basmati rice are a good carbohydrate fix because as little as a half cup is very filling and has a much higher nutritional value than white rice as well as a lower glycemic index factor. Mixing pinto beans with rice creates a complete protein and a low-calorie alternative to meat. Adding a little low-fat cheese to rice and beans mixed with fresh herbs, garlic, and salsa or low-salt Italian diced tomatoes is delicious.

27. Trim the fat from all meat and avoid eating the skin on poultry.

28. Make your own salad dressings, such as balsamic vinegar with a little fresh garlic and some stevia. In restaurants, use straight balsamic vinegar or lemon juice.

29. Vinegar, citrus fruits, and pineapple are great substitutes for salt and flavor on just about anything, and they add very low to no calories.

30. Spaghetti squash and zucchini are excellent substitutes for pasta. They have very few calories and taste like whatever you add to it.

31. "Clean your plate" is one of the worst habits we are taught.

Stop eating when you feel full and save the rest for leftovers.

32. The best way to limit your serving size is to cook at home where you can control the amount of food on your plate.

33. If you must have a high-calorie food at a meal, eat the more nutritious, low-calorie foods on your plate first then you likely won't eat as much of the high-calorie food.

34. Substitute lower-calorie fish for beef.

35. If you can't live without fries, skip the oil and make baked sweet potato fries.

36. Say no to fried and breaded chicken and opt for grilled chicken instead.

37. If you must eat pizza, use a paper towel to blot away some of the greasy fat before you dig in.

38. Put less food on your plate than you think you need. You can always go back to the kitchen for more if you are still hungry, but you might find that you feel full with less food.

39. Never order salad with the dressing already tossed. Get it on the side, so you are in control of how much you eat, and dip your fork in it before you grab the salad mix. You will likely cut the calories from the dressing in half — or even more — and miss none of the taste.

40. When you use olive oil and vinegar on salad, liberally put the vinegar on first, then add just a few drops of olive oil. You will likely cut more than 100 calories from your meal.

41. Use less fat and sugar when cooking.

42. Change the proportion of ingredients so that the same amount of food has more vegetables and fruits, which are filling and low in calories.

SNACKS

43. Switch to plain yogurt and add you own fruit. You can get the health benefits from yogurt and eliminate calories and unwanted sugar.

44. Bring low-calorie snacks to school or work. I like raw broccoli, cauliflower, carrots, snap peas, celery, and red bell peppers. I may also bring a measured portion of almond butter or mashed avocado with garlic powder as a dip. It is important not to let yourself get hungry.

45. Eat a medium-sized apple shortly after meals. The fiber will help you continue to feel full hours later.

46. When you make popcorn, put half of it away to eat for another time.

47. For people who have a sweet tooth like me, eat a small portion of something sweet, like an apple or dark chocolate, so that you can have something satisfying without feeling like you are depriving yourself.

48. Choose crunchy things. Scientists say the more you chew, the longer it takes to eat and the more time your body has to realize that it is full. Snacks that offer a big crunch include carrots, apples, snap peas, and nuts (processed carbohydrates like sugar cereals and candy don't count). They keep your mouth busy longer so you don't inhale your food like a vacuum cleaner.

49. Read the fine print. To get the real scoop on a snack, check out the back of the box. When you see a list of hard-to-pronounce ingredients, there is a greater chance something artificial is mixed in that is not necessarily waistline-friendly. A shorter list usually indicates a more nutritious and slimming pick.

50. Choose air-popped popcorn instead of oil-popped popcorn.

51. Go for dry-roasted nuts instead of the oil-roasted kind.

52. Avoid the vending machine by packing your own healthful snacks to bring to work. For example, consider vegetable sticks, fresh fruit, low-fat or nonfat yogurt without added sugars, or a small handful of dry-roasted nuts.

53. Every morning, prepare a ½-gallon sack of mixed raw vegetables and munch on them throughout the day. It will help keep you from snacking on random things due to uncontrolled hunger.

54. Avoid snacking in front of the TV because we often eat mindlessly when we are watching TV.

55. Have a single piece of dark chocolate after dinner instead of a whole dessert. A little bit of dark chocolate a day has healthy benefits, including increasing blood flow to the brain and decreasing blood pressure, but make sure you count the calories.

56. Have frozen blueberries with nonfat yogurt and a little stevia topped with fat-free whipped cream for dessert — delicious and low in calories.

57. Satisfy sweet-tooth cravings with a cup of hot or iced fruity tea with a little stevia.

58. Fluff up your food. In one study from Penn State, 28 men drank one of three different kinds of milkshakes before lunch. All three milkshakes had the same ingredients, but some were blended longer to add air and volume. The men who drank the "airy" shakes ate 12 percent fewer calories at lunch. And they did not make up for it by eating more at dinner, meaning they kept those calories off. So if you must snack, trick your senses by filling up on an air-filled treat like low-fat frozen yogurt or butter-free popcorn.

BEVERAGES

59. Switch to water first thing in the morning instead of fruit juice.

Fruit juice is high in sugar and calories.

60. Stop drinking soda. Regular sodas are filled with sugar and caffeine. The artificial sweeteners from diet sodas may be harmful to your health, plus because they are up to 600 times sweeter than sugar they may activate the appetite centers of the brain making you crave even more food.

61. Replace sodas with real fruit-flavored water, just like when you are at the spa. My favorite drink is water with lemon juice and a little lemon-flavored stevia, a healthier natural sweetener. It has no calories and it tastes like lemonade. You can do it with oranges, limes, watermelon, etc. This is an easy way to dramatically increase your water intake.

62. Don't let the sport drinks and vitamin waters fake you out. The truth is most are just sweetened water.

63. Don't let beverage labels pull a fast one on you. If it is not water, skim milk, coffee, or tea, it is dessert.

64. Limit alcohol, especially mixed drinks, which can have an outrageous number of calories. For example, one margarita can have as many as 700 calories! Plus, the alcohol decreases prefrontal cortex function, which means your judgment will be impaired, making you more likely to eat more high-fat, high-sugar, high-calorie foods.

65. Limit fat storage by drinking green tea, which contains the antioxidant epigallocatechin gallate (EGCG), shown to boost metabolic rate. In a recent three-month study, participants who took green tea extract lost 4.6 percent of their body weight without changing their diet. To get the benefit, drink at least three cups a day. My favorite is Tropical Acai Berry Green Tea by Celestial Seasonings.

66. Before meals, drink fiber — such as Citrucel, Metamucil, or Miralax (with lots of water) — because it fills the belly, so there is less room for food."

67. When you get hungry, first drink a full glass of water and then if you are still hungry, eat. Many people confuse being dehydrated with being hungry.

68. Use almond milk instead of cow's milk. Blue Diamond unsweetened almond milk contains only 40 calories for 8 ounces. Their unsweetened chocolate almond contains only 45 calories and is delicious. I actually like almond milk better than cow's milk.

69. Using stevia is a great no-calorie way to sweeten drinks, like coffee and tea, and most foods. The best part about stevia is that it is 100 percent natural, and it has no effect on blood sugar.

EATING OUT, PARTIES, AND EVENTS

70. Split meals with your spouse or friends when you eat out.

71. If you are eating out by yourself, put half your meal in a "to go" bag before you even start eating. That way, you won't be tempted to clean your plate.

72. In restaurants, ask if you can substitute a broth-based soup or a green lettuce salad for French fries or chips as a side dish.

73. When eating out, have a cocktail or dessert instead of both during the same meal.

74. After family gatherings, immediately give away or discard any foods that are not on your everyday diet. If the food is perfectly good, take it to your local food bank.

75. Eat a snack or a light meal before you go to a party so you won't be hungry when faced with high-calorie hors d'oeuvres.

76. Skip the bread they serve before meals in restaurants.

77. Don't order appetizers before your entrée.

78. Tell your waiter "No croutons" on your salad.

ANYTIME

79. Use your brain to always think "high-quality calories in." Focus on CRON (calorie restricted and optimally nutritious) foods when you are deciding what to eat.

80. Stay away from "anti-nutrition foods" — such as trans fats, empty calories, or potentially harmful food additives — even if they are low calorie.

81. One of the best ways to cut calories is to write down and measure everything you eat until you are confident that you really know how many calories you put into your body every day. Seeing is believing.

82. Serve your food on smaller plates, which will help to shrink your serving sizes. According to a recent study, the more food you have on your plate, the more you will consume. The opposite is also true.

83. Substitute low-fat cheese — such as string cheese, provolone, or mozzarella —for high-fat cheeses.

84. Substitute lower-fat meats — such as turkey, chicken, or lean pork — for higher-fat, higher-calorie alternatives.

85. Lean on low-density foods to help you feel fuller faster, such as three ounces of strawberries versus three ounces of potato chips. Eat more produce, whole grains, and legumes as opposed to fatty, sugary foods.

86. Chew each bite 20 times. Try to savor the food. In essence, you are performing a mindful meditation when you eat. This also makes your food taste sweeter. Saliva has an enzyme called amylase that breaks down simple carbohydrates, such as wheat or potatoes into sugar.

87. Eat with your fork in your non-dominant hand to reduce dexterity and slow down the shoveling of food into your mouth.

88. Put down your fork after each bite.

89. Cut down on the variety you eat, so that you actually know what is in your food. Gorillas tend to eat the same thing, over and over, and they are obviously strong and muscular. According to the National Zoo, here are the main ingredients of their diet: "The morning diet is generally made up of vegetables, which may include kale, celery, green beans, carrots, and sweet potato. Evening foods include more greens such as romaine, kale, cabbage, or dandelion along with the fruits and vegetables du jour. Bananas, apples, oranges, mango, grapes, melon, and papaya are often included. Onions, broccoli, turnips, white potatoes, squash, cucumbers, and beets are also included. Throughout the day, the gorillas are given additional forage items, such as popcorn, peanuts, or jungle mix. Browse (fresh tree trimmings) is given daily and includes bamboo, Bradford pear, willow, mulberry, or maple."

90. Learn to eyeball servings. After you spend some time weighing food, learn about serving sizes. A three-ounce serving of meat, poultry, or fish is about the size of a deck of cards, two servings of pasta or rice is the size of a baseball, a bread serving is the size of a CD case, and one serving of cheese is the size of four dice.

91. Eat at the table. A study in the *Journal of the American Dietetic Association* found that 59 percent of young women eat on the go, and on-the-run eaters consume more total fat as well as more soda and fast food. The less distracted and stressed you are when you dine, the more efficiently your body absorbs nutrients. Eat at the table and focus on your food not the TV or traffic.

92. For virtually no calories, adding spice to your meals can increase your metabolism. Different studies have shown that

spicy foods can increase your metabolism by 8 to 20 percent for at least 30 minutes after eating. A little bit of cayenne pepper or cinnamon is all you need to add to your favorite recipes.

93. Eat veggies at every meal. When people eat vegetables with a meal, they consume a full 20 percent fewer calories overall while feeling satisfied, according to a study from the *American Journal of Clinical Nutrition*.

94. Eat raw fruits and veggies that are high in fiber. Your body has to burn a lot of calories to break these down, plus they will give you longer-lasting energy while fighting off hunger cravings, which means you can get skinny while your body burns fat! Researchers at Tufts University found that the more vegetables people eat, the thinner they are.

95. Increase your fiber. Eating fiber helps to prevent overeating because it makes you feel full. You will have an even greater feeling of fullness and higher energy levels throughout the day if you eat meals that are mostly made up of fiber, protein, and water. Fiber also slows down the digestion of foods you eat, keeping your blood sugar and energy levels in check and preventing you from getting hungry. Good sources of fiber are vegetables, fruits, nuts, beans, and some cereals. The amount of fiber in a food product is listed in the nutritional facts found on most food labels. Fiber takes so long to be digested by your body, a person eating 20 to 35 grams of fiber a day will burn an extra 150 calories a day or lose 16 extra pounds a year.

96. Make sure you eat healthy fats with every meal. It helps with satiety and serves to curb your appetite between meals. An Australian study showed that eating a meal with healthy fats, such as olive oil, significantly increased fat-burning rate five hours later, particularly in subjects with more abdominal fat.

97. Measure the foods that you tend to overeat.

98. Buying a food scale to measure portion sizes and buying food

in prepared-portioned sizes helps keep calories down.

99. Make sure you have enough calcium in your diet. Researchers have linked calcium with lower production of the stress-hormone cortisol (remember cortisol switches the body into a fat-storing mode). According to several studies, people who increase their calcium intake lose more weight than people with low calcium levels. Sources of calcium include yogurt, ricotta cheese, and spinach.

100. Consistently reduce your meal sizes by just 10 percent. You won't even notice, and it will save an amazing number of calories.

APPENDIX C

Natural Supplements To Heal The Brain

In treating people, one question I always ask myself is what would I prescribe if this were my mother, my wife, or my child? More and more, after nearly 30 years of being a psychiatrist, I find myself recommending natural treatments. I am not opposed to medications and I have prescribed them for a long time, but I want you to use all of the tools available, especially if they are effective, less expensive and have fewer side effects.

The Pros and Cons of Supplements

To start, the benefit of natural supplements is that they are often effective. They have dramatically fewer side effects than most prescription medications and they are significantly less expensive. Plus, you never have to tell an insurance company that you have taken them. As awful as it sounds, taking prescription medications can affect your insurability. I know many people who have been denied or made to pay higher rates for insurance because they have taken certain medications. If there are natural alternatives, they are worth considering.

Yet, natural supplements also have their own set of problems. Even though they tend to be less expensive than medications, they may be more expensive for you because they are usually not covered by insurance. Many people are unaware that natural supplements can have side effects and need to be thoughtfully used. Just because something is natural does not mean it is innocuous. Both arsenic and cyanide are natural, but that doesn't mean they are good for you. For example, St. John's wort, one of my favorite natural antidepressants, can cause sun sensitivity and it can also decrease the effectiveness of a number of medications such as birth control pills. Oh great! Get depressed, take St. John's wort from the grocery store, now you are pregnant when you don't want to be. That may not be a good thing.

One of the major concerns about natural supplements is the lack of quality control. There is variability, and you need to find brands you trust. Another disadvantage is that many people get their advice about supplements from the teenage clerk at the health food store who may not have the best information. But, even when looking at the problems, the benefits of natural supplements make them worth considering, especially if you can get thoughtful, research-based information.

Every day I personally take a handful of supplements that I know make a significant difference in my life. They have changed the health of my brain, my energy, and my lab values. Many physicians say that if you eat a balanced diet you do not need supplements. I love what Dr. Mark Hyman wrote in his book *The UltraMind Solution: Fix Your Broken Brain by Healing Your Body First.* He wrote that if people "eat wild, fresh, organic, local, non-genetically modified food grown in virgin mineral- and nutrient-rich soils that has not been transported across vast distances and stored for months before being eaten... and work and live outside, breathe only fresh unpolluted air, drink only pure, clean water, sleep nine hours a night, move their bodies every day, and are free from chronic stressors and exposure to environmental toxins," then it is possible that they might not need supplements. Because we live in a fast-paced society where we pick up food on the fly, skip meals, eat sugar-laden treats, buy processed foods, and eat foods that have been chemically treated, we could all use a little help from a multiple vitamin/mineral supplement.

Amen Clinics Supplements

At the Amen Clinics we make our own line of supplements that have taken over a decade to develop. The reason I developed this line was that I wanted my patients and my own family to have access to the highest quality, research-based supplements available. After I started recommending supplements to my patients they would go to the supermarket, drug store, or health food store and have so many choices that they would not know what or how to choose. Plus, there is variability of quality in the supplements available. Another reason I developed my own line was that the Amen Clinics sees a high population of people who have attention deficit disorder. I realized if they did not get their supplements as they walked out the door, they would forget about it or procrastinate and not have started them by their next appointment.

Research shows the therapeutic benefit of using supplements in treating mild to moderate depression, insomnia, weight issues, and cognitive impairment. We strongly recommend that when purchasing a supplement, you consult your health care practitioner to determine what dosage would be most effective for you. Our website (www.amenclinics.com) contains links to the scientific literature on every product, so you, as a consumer, can be fully informed on the benefits and risks involved. Please remember supplements can have very powerful effects on the body and caution should be used when combining them with prescription medications.

Here is a list of some of our bestselling supplements to help for brain recovery, cravings, energy, focus, and mood control.

Dr. Daniel Amen's Nutraceutical Solutions: NeuroVite +
This supplement contains a high-potency multiple vitamin/mineral supplement, plus nutrients targeted to enhance overall brain function.

Dr. Daniel Amen's Nutraceutical Solutions: Omega-3 Power
High-quality fish oil that contains a balance between EPA and DHA.

Dr. Daniel Amen's Nutraceutical Solutions: Brain & Memory Power Boost
Contains nutrients targeted to enhance memory and encourage overall brain healing.

Dr. Daniel Amen's Nutraceutical Solutions: Restful Sleep
Proper sleep is a critical component to a brain healthy program. In our formula, we use several scientifically-based ingredients to enhance restorative sleep.

Dr. Daniel Amen's Nutraceutical Solutions: Craving Control
This solution is formulated to decrease cravings by balancing blood sugar and decreasing compulsive behaviors.

Dr. Daniel Amen's Nutraceutical Solutions: Serotonin Mood Support
This formula is designed to enhance serotonin in the brain to promote a healthy mood.

Dr. Daniel Amen's Nutraceutical Solutions: Focus & Energy Optimizer
This formula was designed to enhance focus and energy.

Dr. Daniel Amen's Nutraceutical Solutions: SAMe Mood & Movement Support
This formula is designed to enhance a positive mood and energy.

Dr. Daniel Amen's Nutraceutical Solutions: GABA Calming Support
This GABA-based formula was made to help lower anxiety and stress.

Dr. Daniel Amen's Weight-Loss Solutions

⬦ Basic Formula – *Craving Control*

⬦ Type 1: The Compulsive Overeater – doubles as *Serotonin Mood Support*

⬦ Type 2: The Impulsive Overeater – doubles as *Focus & Energy Optimizer*

⬦ Type 3: The Impulsive-Compulsive Overeater – combines Types 1 & 2

⬦ Type 4: The SAD Overeater – doubles as *SAMe Mood & Movement Support*

⬦ Type 5: The Anxious Overeater – doubles as *GABA Calming Support*

ABOUT THE AUTHOR

Daniel G. Amen, M.D., is a physician, child and adult psychiatrist, brain-imaging specialist, and *New York Times* bestselling author. He is the writer, producer, and host of four highly successful public television programs, raising more than 20 million dollars for public television. He is a Distinguished Fellow of the American Psychiatric Association and the CEO and medical director of Amen Clinics in Newport Beach and Fairfield, California; Tacoma, Washington; and Reston, Virginia.

Amen Clinics is the world leader in applying brain-imaging science to everyday clinical practice and has the world's largest database of functional scans related to behavior, now totaling more than 55,000.

Dr. Amen is the author of 35 professional scientific articles and 24 books, including the *New York Times* bestsellers, *Change Your Brain, Change Your Life* and *Magnificent Mind At Any Age*. He is also the author of *Healing ADD*, *Healing the Hardware of the Soul*, *Making a Good Brain Great*, *The Brain In Love*, and the co-author of *Healing Anxiety And Depression* and *Preventing Alzheimer's*. Newsmax publishes Dr. Amen's monthly newsletter.

Dr. Amen has appeared on the Dr. Oz Show, the Today Show, Good Morning America, The View, Larry King, The Early Show, CNN, HBO, Discovery Channel, and many other national television and radio programs. His national public television shows include Change Your Brain, Change Your Life; Magnificent Mind At Any Age; The Brain In Love; and Change Your Brain, Change Your Body.